The
Green Man
of Knowledge

and other
Scots traditional
tales

The Green Man of Knowledge

and other
Scots traditional
tales

from tape-recordings in the archives
of the School of Scottish Studies
University of Edinburgh

selected and edited by Alan Bruford

ABERDEEN UNIVERSITY PRESS

First published 1982
Aberdeen University Press
A member of the Pergamon Group

© School of Scottish Studies, University of Edinburgh 1982

British Library Cataloguing in Publication Data
The Green Man of Knowledge and other Scots
    traditional tales
    1. Tales, Scottish
    I. Bruford, Alan
    398.2'1'09411   GR144

    ISBN 0-08-025757-7
    ISBN 0-08-025758-5   Pbk

Design and illustrations by AUP Graphics

PRINTED IN GREAT BRITAIN
AT THE UNIVERSITY PRESS
ABERDEEN

Contents

INTRODUCTION · vii

PRINCIPLES OF TRANSCRIPTION · xi

The Tales

One-Eye, Two-Eyes and Three-Eyes · 1

The Robbers and the Old Woman · 8

The Green Man of Knowledge · 11

The King and the Miller · 28

The Three Dogs · 31

The Parson's Sheep · 39

The Cat and the Hard Cheese · 41

Cheeseparer and Teastrainer · 54

Jack and the Devil's Purse · 55

The Devil at the Foul Ford · 61

The Angel of Death · 63

The Bridegroom and the Skull · 68

Contents

The Three Yells · 72

The Death of James Smith · 74

Some Orkney Weather · 78

The Trow of Windhouse · 80

The Oo-T'iggers · 85

The Milk and Butter Stones · 87

Witch Meets Witch · 91

Peerie Merran's Spoon · 92

The Magic Island · 93

Mallie Coutts' Fairy Boy · 95

The Last Trow in Yell · 97

STORYTELLERS · 99

NOTES · 103

GLOSSARY · 116

Introduction

The collection of Gaelic folktales in Scotland began with John Francis Campbell of Islay in 1859, and since then thousands of them have been taken down in writing or more recently recorded on cylinder, disc, wire or tape by his many followers. The collection of Lowland Scots folktales began with Robert Chambers and Peter Buchan nearly fifty years earlier, and the twenty-nine stories which appeared in Chambers' *Popular Rhymes of Scotland* and Buchan's long unpublished *Ancient Scottish Tales* showed every sign of being almost the sum total that would ever be found. In fact, though very few more international wonder-tales (*Märchen*, "fairy-tales" set in a timeless world of kings and woodcutters) were taken down until recently, the more realistic local supernatural and historical legends and short anecdotes have continued to circulate in oral tradition: some of them have been published by local enthusiasts in the Northern Isles, Galloway or the North-East in the dialect in which they were told, but many more have appeared in summary form in local histories and travelogues.

More systematic enquiries by the School of Scottish Studies (a department of the University of Edinburgh founded in 1951) with some help from independent collectors, from bodies such as the Shetland Folk Society and more recently from local radio stations, have proved that it is still possible to find such legends and comic anecdotes with ease in Shetland, with rather more effort in most other non-Gaelic-speaking districts. But also, while the Gaelic tradition at last shows signs of being squeezed dry, and we may have lost the last teller of long heroic tales, a trickle of Scots wonder-tales first tapped in the fifties among the travelling people or tinkers is now becoming a torrent, and now for the first time since 1859 more interesting traditional tales are being collected in Scots than in Gaelic. The stories printed here are only first-fruits of a rich harvest.

The reasons for the unsuspected survival of these stories must be connected with the circumstances in which they were told. It is worth emphasising that most folktales in Lowland Scotland, as in the Highlands and Ireland and at one time throughout Europe, were an evening entertainment for adults. There were certain stories only told by mothers to children at bedtime, but "household tales", as the brothers Grimm called them, were listened to by everyone at the fireside—women spinning or knitting, men perhaps mending nets or harness or winding ropes, only the children who managed to stay up on the fringes of the circle idle—until a time came when Victorian rationalism drove out the ability to suspend disbelief in the wonderful, and increased literacy and the availability of books and newspapers replaced song and spoken story as the first choice for entertainment. Fireside storytelling was probably universal throughout rural Scotland about 1800, and had vanished as a normal entertainment in most places a hundred years later, though the singing of songs and ballads—most of them also telling a story—might linger longer, until replaced by gramophone and radio. In the Highlands ceilidhing, regular evening visiting by neighbours to enjoy song and story as well as gossip and card-playing, kept the tradition going into the years between the Wars, and the Shetland equivalent, coming "in aboot da nyht", lasted almost as long and kept alive a great range of stories. Among the travelling people, especially where several families were camped together at the berry-picking or tattie-howking, or just after a chance encounter on the road, the fireside and its stories remained an even more central part of their life.

All folklore is, virtually by definition, claimed as the property of the group which remembers it. Shetlanders anchor their stories to actual places if not to historical persons and tell them in a half-Norse dialect which is "broader" than any other form of Scots, though the plots of the stories may at times be known from China to Chile. Similarly the travellers use their own cant to some extent in stories told among themselves (though they will drop most of it for an outside audience) and claim that these are "old traveller tales". Sometimes they are indeed modified, to make Cinderella, say, a traveller girl who marries a gentleman with the help of her magic granny, or at least to incorporate the travellers' world view, half sentimental, half fiercely independent. There are also specifically traveller legends, notably about the "Burkers" who, as most travellers firmly believe, still go around in coaches with muffled wheels and top-hatted medical students on the step looking for vagrants to murder in the manner of Burke and Hare so that their bodies can be dissected. Outside these legends of their own the travellers know relatively few of the firmly localised tales of fairies, witches, apparitions and bad landlords which were the staple diet of farm and croft firesides a century or two ago. Instead they have preserved many of the international folktales, rootless wanderers like themselves, which other Lowlanders have lost. But the versions which they have preserved are mostly Lowland Scots ones, with Scots "runs" or descriptive formulae and turns of phrase in them. A few evidently have come from Gaelic or from popular books—Grimm, Andersen, even retold Greek myths—but we can be fairly sure that the greater part of the repertoire descends from the fireside tales of eighteenth-century Lowland Scotland. And both in range and style this is the richest repertoire of these international folktales yet found in any variation of the English language, easily outclassing the few remnants from England, certainly far outnumbering the Anglo-Irish examples yet published (though these have been under-collected in comparison with the Irish Gaelic) and even surpassing the store of fine but generally short folktales recently uncovered in mountainous areas of North America such as the Appalachians and the Ozarks.

All these stories have been preserved in Scotland because they had some importance to the storytellers, as part of the traditions of their own family and community and because situations existed where the storytellers could still practice them on an audience other than themselves. Most of the storytellers represented here have tried out their techniques on enough audiences to tell their tales with some artistry. Often they visualise the scenes they are telling about clearly in their mind's eye and describe them in vivid detail. Some pay careful attention to recreating the time-hallowed phrases which they heard from their parents; others reel off a racy colloquial patter which is all their own. Some have told us that they will tell a story differently to different audiences—fellow-tinkers, children, students or folklorists—and even vary names and other details to keep up the interest for themselves. Some will put together new stories from elements of others they know, or add in a new episode *ad lib*; most of them at least enjoy inventing interesting and well characterised conversations between the actors in the story.

This collection is intended to give samples of the main varieties of traditional tales still to be collected in Scots: international wonder-tales for adults and children; tales of luck and cleverness; legends of the Devil, witches, fairies and the dead; tall tales and anecdotes. However, the long wonder-tales, of a sort which most people in this country expect to be translated from another language, are the most remarkable and form the core of the book. Some parts of the storyteller's technique cannot well be put down on paper; the inflections of the voice, the onomatopoeia, the variations in speed and loudness of narration, the dramatic pauses, even the stutters and repetitions may be effective, and then there is the hand laid on your arm, the dramatic gestures, the hypnotic gaze, the "presence" of the first-rate storyteller. The reader must supply these from his own imagination and the hints in the wording. Most of the stories in the present volume have previously appeared in *Scottish Studies* and *Tocher*, the journals of the School of Scottish Studies, and are reprinted by permission of the editors. Two others, "One-Eye, Two-Eyes and Three-Eyes" and "The Angel of Death", have been prepared for a two-disc album of Scots tales which it is hoped will be the next in the Scottish Tradition series of records produced by Tangent Records; this will enable readers to hear the voices of Betsy Whyte and Stanley Robertson, along with eight other storytellers of whom Tom Tulloch, James Henderson, Jeannie Robertson and Bella Higgins are also represented, though by different stories, in this book.

Principles of Transcription

All the stories are transcribed from tape-recordings in the Sound Archive of the School of Scottish Studies, and are copyright by the School on behalf of the storytellers or their heirs: in the tape-number quoted in the notes to each tale, the figure following the letters SA (Sound Archive) is the year of recording. Other details are given in the notes. All the stories were transcribed by the editor, except the second and third in the book, where the orthography of the distinguished poets involved has been standardised and details checked with the tape since the first publication.

The transcriptions do not exactly follow any established convention for the spelling of Scots (if any can be called established) though the principle of cutting down on apostrophes suggested by the Makars' Club in 1947 is generally adhered to. The aim has been a compromise between indicating the exact sound of the spoken word—not an easy task using the limited resources of English orthography, especially when dealing with vowel sounds—and departing as little as possible from the standard English spelling, to make it easier for the non-Scots to follow.

Doubled vowels show length—*aa* for long *a*, *ee* for phonetic long *i*, *oo* for phonetic long *u*. In words from the Northern Isles *ö* and *ü* are approximately as in German; *ā* represents an *a* shorter or more fronted than the *a* in a corresponding standard English word; *ë* is a diaeresis to separate the *e* from the preceding vowel.

Unstressed words and syllables are normally spelt as in English unless there is a pretty clear difference in sound: "singin" rather than the historically correct "singan", "would" rather than "wad" in most cases. To avoid ambiguity "ow" or "oo" are used in the middle of words rather than "ou". Front long *e* (French *é*) is written for preference as *ai*, and the back form (*è*) as *ae*, but the Scots form of "heart" is written neither phonetically accurately as "hairt", nor in the usual form "hert" (which might suggest the pronunciation of "hurt"), but as "haert" because this suggests the direction of the sound-shift with the least alteration of the English spelling. The Shetland convention of writing *d* for voiced *th*, with "da" for "the", can mostly be ignored because the storytellers in this book generally use at least a slightly different sound for "there" from that in "dare"; the unvoiced equivalent more often sounds like *t*, but the apostrophe in "t'ink" will point to the English "think".

The language, except in some of the Shetland examples, is easier than Burns' Scots, and probably most non-Scots know enough to follow a sentence like "Set ye doon, ye're a richt bonnie wee lassie." However, most words involving differences of more than one letter (altered, transposed or omitted) from standard English are noted in the Glossary, along with the most frequent single-letter changes. Centuries of Scots-English bilingualism have meant that even a single person's language may include two or more forms of a word—"our" and "oor", "bannock" and "bonnick", "hame", "hom" or "heem" in the Northern Isles; and at least fifteen different Scots forms in the book are used for the four words "go", "went", "going" and "gone". Dialect peculiarities to look out for include the North-East's love of the long *ee* sound and tendency among some speakers to drop initial *th* (so "'ere" is "there", not "here"), and in Shetland the alternation between *qu* and *wh*, so that in some districts you hear of "a quite beard" and in others "white true": sometimes one hears an intermediate sound for which I have used the old Scots *quh*. Some difficulties may be caused not by Scots forms but by outdated English slang or sheer bad grammar. On the other hand Scots grammar and syntax *are* different, especially in verbal forms and such questions as the use of a singular verb with a plural noun as subject, or double negatives: so there is nothing wrong with, say, "Ones 'at kens them telled me this men hasnae done nothing," or in the Northern Isles, "What says thu?" "I'm seen it!" (never "I've" in the islands). A good brief introduction to the peculiarities of Scots is David Murison's *The Guid Scots Tongue* (Edinburgh 1977). But these are first and foremost stories in living Scots, and it would be a shame to spoil their liveliness by pausing too often to look up exact meanings: I hope the reader may catch a hint of how they sounded, but above all enjoy them.

One-Eye, Two-Eyes and Three-Eyes

Betsy Whyte

Once upon a time there wis this woman and she hed three dochters. Two o them wis her ain dochters, but the ither one wis a step-dochter, the youngest one. Noo this woman wisnae like ony ither woman, because she had four eyes: she had one in her foreheid, an one at the back o her heid, an one at every side. An her ain twa dochters were odd tae: one o them had jist one eye in the middle o the forehead and the ither one had three eyes, one in the middle an one at each side. Now this two dochters an this woman, they didnae like this stepdochter because she wis normal an hed two eyes, so they made her dae aa the dirty work aboot the place, and seldom gien her anything but a wee drap watery porridge tae eat; an she'd tae go away every day up this hill, an away up for miles, and watch the sheep an the goats.

Now this wee lassie used tae sit up there every day withoot a bite or anything, except maybe ony berries or onything she got when it wis the season fir them, ye ken? But she hed a wee goat o her ain, it wis a wee pet goat, it wis the sharger, so they didnae mind her gettin it, an she used tae sit an cuddle it an kiss it an cairry on wi it an speak tae it as if it wis a buddy she wis wi, ye ken? Because she wis sae weariet up this hill. But one day she wis sittin up there, strokin her wee goat, an lookin efter the sheep an the other goats, when wha did she see comin alang the road but a funny wee man? An he wis aafae wee, this man, she thocht, an he didnae seem tae walk, ye ken, he seemed tae jist lilt alang the grund. An he came up tae her an he says, "Hullo," he says, "ma dear," he says, "whit are yeze doin up here?"

She says, "Oh, A'm jist mindin ma sheep an goats an that," she said.

He says, "But whit are ye lookin fir?"

"Oh," she says, "A wis lookin fir berries."

He says, "A doot ye'll no get nae mair berries ony mair the year then." He says, "Are ye hungry?"

1

"Oh," she says, "A'm stairvin!"

"Well," he says, "A'll show ye whit tae dae." He says, "D'ye see yir wee goat there?" He says, "Go tae yir wee goat, an stroke its ear, an say:

> 'Bleat, little goat, bleat,
> And bring me something nice tae eat!'"

He says, "Go on, dae it now!"

So she went an stroked her wee goat's ear, and she said:

> "Bleat, little goat, bleat,
> And bring me something nice tae eat!"

An no sooner said than the deed wis done: there, spread on the gress, wis a table-cover, an it wis jist laden wi all the nicest things ye could think aboot tae eat—fruit, an everything. An he says, "Now eat!"

An she says, "Whit aboot you, will you no take something wi me?"

He says, "Aye, A'll take something wi ye." So the two o them sat doon an they ate an ate an ate, and she wis—jist rived intae it, she wis that hungry, ye ken? And . . . there wis still lots left, an she says, "Whit am A gaunnae dae wi this noo?"

He says, "Well, jist stroke yir wee goat's ear again, and say:

> 'Bay, little goat, bay,
> And take the nice things all away.'"

So she went tae her wee goat, an she stroked its ear an stroked its ear, an said:

> "Bay, little goat, bay,
> And take the nice things all away."

Noo that nicht when she come hame—ye ken?—an saw this watery porridge, she says, "Ah, A'm no hungry," she says, "mither, A'm no wantin nothing tae eat," she says, "A'm tired, A'm gaun awa tae ma bed."

But every day now, when she went up, sittin up there herdin her goats an sheep, she would dae this wi the wee goat, an she would get as much as she could eat, an it wis lovely every day. An when she come hame, she wouldnae take the porridge, ye see. So this stepmother o hirs says tae her ither twa dochters, she says, "It's aafae funny hoo she's no takkin the

3

porridge," she says. "She must be gettin something tae eat some place," she says. "And she's growin bonny an her skin's growin glowin," she says, "an she's lookin sae healthy she must be gettin meat some way," she says, "so A want one o yeze tae go wi her the morn, an watch an see whar she's gettin the meat." So she says, "You, One-Eye, " she says, "you go wi her the morn."

So the next mornin One-Eye says, "A'm comin wi ye the day, Two-Eyes."

She says, "Oh, that's fine." She wis gled o any company, she wis that much on her own, ye see? So the two o them's sittin up this hill, an playin an makin daisy chains, and singin, an cairryin on an makin fun, ye see, as lassies will, and little Two-Eyes, she startit singin. An she wis singin an singin away till One-Eye fell sound asleep listenin tae her singin. An when she got her sleepin, she went tae her wee goat, and she says:

> "Bleat, little goat, bleat,
> An bring me something nice tae eat."

And there wis the table-cover an all the goodies. So she filled hersel, and said:

> "Bay, little goat, bay,
> And take the good things all away."

An they jist went away again.

When they come hame that nicht, an this woman says to One-Eye, "Well, did ye see noo whar she wis gettin anything tae eat?"

"No," she says, "I never seen her gettin anything."

"Are ye sure?" she says.

"Aye, A'm sure," she says. "She never got nothing the day, onywey."

She says, "Were ye there aa the time?"

"Aye, A wis there aa the time," she says. "Whar wis A gan tae gang tae?"

"Are ye sure?"

"Well," she says, "A wis sleepin fir twa 'r three minutes, richt enough. A fell asleep," she said.

"Ach," she says, "A canna trust ye at aa," she says. "A'm goin tae pit Three-Eyes up there the morn, 'cause A'm sure she's gettin something some wey, she wouldnae be lookin sae good."

So the next day she put Three-Eyes up tae watch her. An Three-Eyes come up wi her, an they played aboot an cairried on, an wee Two-Eyes was singin an singin away, an Three-Eyes fell asleep. But it wis only two o her eyes that slept: the other eye wis wide open, this eye in the middle, an it was kind o covered wi her hair, ye ken? So wee Two-Eyes, she didnae ken this, and she went up tae her wee goat an said:

> "Bleat, little goat, bleat,
> An bring me something nice tae eat!"

And she filled hersel an said:

> "Bay, little goat, bay,
> An take the nice things all away!"

Noo that night when they went hame Three-Eyes couldnae get rinnin tae tell her mither quick enough.

"Oh," she says, "that's whit it is, is it? A'll suin put an end tae that!" So she went and she tell't the gairdner fir tae kill the goat. So the gairdner went an he killed the goat, an wee Two-Eyes, she wis—she tell't her she wis gaen tae dae it, she says, "That goat's gettin killed!"—an she wis aboot demented aboot her wee goat. And she run away oot an away runnin here an there—she didnae ken whar she wis gan, she wis that agitatit an upset aboot her wee goat. An wha did she meet but this wee man again? An he says, "Whit's adae wi ye, Two-Eyes?"

"Oh," she says, "they've killed ma goat," she says, "they've killed ma wee goat." She says, "Three-Eyes found oot that I wis gettin meat fae it," she says, "an so ma stepmither's killed it."

"Ach," he says, "try an content yirsel," he said. He says, "A'll tell ye whit tae dae. Go in tae yir stepmither," he says, "an ask her if ye can hae the wee goat's haert. A dinnae think she'll keep it back fae ye," he says. "An when ye get it, come oot," he says, "an tak it oot in the gairden, an bury it in the gairden, an," he says, "A think ye'll feel better efter ye dae that."

So in she goes, and she asked her stepmither fir the haert, and she says, "Oh, ye can hae it," she says, "tak it." So she got the wee goat's haert, an she took it oot tae the gairden, and she buried it.

Noo the next mornin when she woke up she wonder't how the sun wis oot sae aerly—ye ken, there wis an aafae bricht licht in the hoose—an she

5

says, "Eh, A've slept in the day, A doot," she says, "A'll hae tae get up quick." And when she got up an pulled back the curtains an looked oot, this wis a tree, pure golden aipples hingin thick on it, near dazzled the een aff her. "My goodness," she says, "that's a bonny aipple tree!" She says, "That's whar I buried ma wee goat's haert."

But she had to run doon anyway, she was that feared o her stepsisters and her stepmither, ye see, she run doon tae get started on her work; and jist like that, wha come alang the road past the hoose but the young prince in a carriage?—six lovely white horses in his carriage—an when he spies this aipple tree, he jist pulls the horses up an shouted tae his man fir tae stop. He says, "I must see who belangs this tree."

So he jumps doon oot o the cairriage, an he went up tae the door an knocked at the door, an the aald woman come oot. An he says, "Is that your tree?"

"Oh, of course it's my tree," she says. "Wha's tree wid it be? This is my hoose."

"Well," he says. "A wonder if you would sell me even one o that apples?"

She says, "A'll suin dae that." So she went ower tae the tree, and she tried reachin up tae the tree, and she tried shakin, tried tae get a branch tae shake, but no: she would reach up, the branches wis goin higher an higher so that she couldnae get tae them.

And he says, "A doot it's no your tree."

She says, "Well, really," she says, "it's one o ma lassies's trees, but I jist coont it ma ain as weel."

He says, "Well, send the lassie oot."

So Three-Eyes she cam oot, an she went up tae the tree, an she tried tae reach—she even tried climbin it, an as she was climbin it the tree wid jist gie itsel a shake an knock her doon.

She says, "It must be the ither lassie it belangs tae." So One-Eye cam oot, an One-Eye wis tryin tae climb up it—she wis fleeter than Three-Eyes, ye see, an the branches jist come *whuch* [guttural noise], knocked her doon. She even fell right doon tae the bottom o the tree.

He says, "I doot nane o you belangs tae this tree." He says, "There naebody else in the hoose?"

They says, "No, there's naebody else," she says. "Naebody but us."

6

But jist like that, one o this aipples fell aff the tree, an it rolled. An it rolled an rolled right tae the back door o the hoose, whar wee Two-Eyes wis standin, back intae the doorway, ye ken, lookin at them. An it rolled an stopped right at her feet, and she bent doon an picked it up, and she took it up tae the prince an she says, "There ye are, there's an aipple tae ye."

He says, "Dae ye think ye could get me any more?"

An she went up tae the tree, an the aipples jist fell doon intae her apron—she jist held it like that an the aipples fell doon intae it. And the prince says, "This must be your tree."

"Yes," she said. She says, "It is my tree."

So the prince says, "Well, whit about you comin wi me," he says, "an bein my bride?"

So she went away wi the prince, an they got marriet an lived happy ever efter!

The Robbers and the Old Woman

Jeannie Robertson

There wis oncet an auld woman: she lived hersel in a little wee hoosie in the country, oh, awaa in the back o beyont, but she wis turnin very, very auld. She wis awaa aboot echty or echty-odds, an 'course she wis gettin a bittie dottle kind o things, an speakin til hersel an one thing an anither. But she wis supposed to hae a lot o money, ye see, hidden in this hoose—a *lot* o money, and she wis real miser tae kind, ye know. And there wis three men come to rob her that nicht, three men. An one o this men wantit a ee, but the three o them wis gan tae help each ither an get the money—steal the money an murder the aald wumman an get awaa wi it, ye see, 'cause it wis in a lonely place. . . .

But it happen't tae be, onywey or anither, that that nicht this poor auld cratur, she'd on the brander (ye know the branders they used to keep on their fire, an some o them has them yet in the country. . . like it was real aald-fashion't: they used to roast their . . . kippers and things upon the branders, you see). And she wis—this aald-fashion't brander on—she wis roasting this kippers fir her supper; but she wis speakin away to the kippers as if they were human beins, you see, as dottle fowk dis, 'cause I sut an watch't it! You see? [laughing] And she's speakin awaa to this kippers, rocking hersel back an forth, ye see, in . . . an aald chair, ower this aul'-fashion't fire, ye see, roastin this kippers an turnin them. . . .

But she didnae ken there wis three men come tae murder her and rob her 'at nicht. But the one o them's comin doon the lum (that wis the wey 'at he wis gaan tae enter, ye see, because the hoose wis aa lockit up, an he wis gaan tae enter comin doon the lum). But she'd this wee bittie o a fire on, ye see, nae very much, twa or three sticks, and she's roastin 'is kipper, the first kipper, and she says: "Ha haa," she says, "there's three o yeze, an there's wan o yeze," she says, "gan awaa," she says, "soon," she says, "fir A'll rost ye an A'll tost ye," she says, "an A'll eat ye fir ma supper!" Ye see?

The Robbers and the Old Woman

Now a lot o them aye said, nae only wis she a miser, but a lot o them said 'at she wis an aald witch. Ye see? Well they believe't it in that days onywey, whether they were or no, they'd only to say it. But . . . there wis a story oot 'at . . . och, years afore, 'at this auld woman wis an aal' witch, you see. And this man, at this time the first een *wis* comin doon the lum when she wis roastin the first kipper, and she's addre—speakin tae the kipper, and she's not speakin tae him at all. She didnae ken aboot a man comin doon the lum, so that's whit she said: "Ha haa," she says, "there's three o yeze, and," she says, "there wan o yeze goin awaa," she says, "but A'll rost ye," she says, "an A'll tost ye an A'll eat ye for ma supper!"

He says, "Goad bless us," he says, "she kens A'm comin doon!" He says, "She's gan tae rost me," he says, "an tost me an eat me fir her supper!"

So he's up the lum an oot, an he—"No, no," he says tae the ither yins, he says, "praise God," he says, "A'm nae gan tae rob her," he says, "or kill her. She kens," he says, "that we're comin doon—'at A wis comin doon her lum: she kent," he says, "we're here. She said there wis three o us, an 'at I wis, eh—ye know!—wan wis gan awaa, an 'at she wis gan tae eat me, an rost me an eat me, ye see, so," he says, "no, no," he says, "A'm nae taen nothin to dae with her!" He's off an away: he got fear't.

Ach, doon the secont yin goes. He says, "He's too yalla," ye see; he says, "She's nae a witch," an aa this an the next thing, but he gaes doon the lum. Now she's rostin the second kipper be this time, and she says, "Haa haa, there wan o yeze awaa," she says, "an ye're—'is is the secont yin to come," she says. "But A'll rost ye an A'll tost ye," she says, "an A'll eat ye fir ma supper!"

But he took a haert-fricht tae, ye see, and he's up the lum: he wonder't whit wey she kent, 'caze naebody see'd them gae near this place, ye see. An he's up the lum an he tells the ither yin, he says, "No, no," he says, "that's a witch richt enough," he says. "She kent," he says, "'at I wis comin, an she wis preparin fir to rost me," he says, "an tost me an eat me fir her supper. . . . So," he says, "no, no," he says, "A'm nae gaen tae hae nothing to dae wi her," so . . . he's away too, he runs away too.

Noo the last yin tae come wantit the eye. But it juist happen't tae be that her last kipper . . . didnae hae a ee ether, it wantit an ee. Well, *we* wouldnae pay a notice whether a kipper had a ee or no, but til an aald dottled buddy like 'is, 'is queer kind o wee ferlies, dis stand out tae them.

So she's pit the kipper on an she's roastin it an turnin it, ye know, an doon comes this man wantin the ee, an he's more desperater, an he's the yin 'at wis gan to murder her. An he's comin doon, quite desperate fir tae kill her an get her money.

"Haa haa!" she says, "come oan," she says, "come awaa! A'm juist waitin for ye!" she says (but it wis her kipper she wis speakin to, to hurry up an roast!). She says, "Juist come awaa," she says . . . "hurry up an come," she says, "A'm waitin upon ye," she says. "Ye're the third yin tae come," she says . . . "an ye want a ee." Now this made it mair convincin tae him when she heard him [*sic*] sayin this. "And," she says, "the third yin wants a ee," she says, "but," she says, "A'll rost ye," she says, "an A'll tost ye an A'll *eat* ye fir ma supper!" (She's beginnin tae get high-kind now, ye see, to this kipper wantin the ee.)

So when he hears this he says, "Goad bless us! It's richt enough," he says, "she even kens A want a ee." So he's up the lum an away.

So it wis only the poor aald dottle't wumman speakin til her three kippers that save't her ain life.

The Green Man of Knowledge

Geordie Stewart

Well, this is a story aboot an old lady—an auld woman—she bred pigs. She wes a widow-woman, an she'd a son cried Jack. An this son wes jist a nitwit, he'd nae sense, they said—so they said, onywey—an he used to sit at the fireside amongst the ashes. Aye, he'd a big auld hairy Hielan collie-dog. An this collie-dog wes aa he look't at an mindit; him an his dog used to sit an play cards—an I couldnae say the dog played back, like—he played cards wi his dog. An that's aa he did, the lee-lang day.

But Jack, he comes to the age of twenty-one. An on his twenty-oneth birthday, . . . he rises fae the fireside an streetches hissel—an he's a man weel over six fit. An his breekies he was wearin fin he did streetch hissel went up to abeen his knees. An his jaicket an schuil-buits . . . he wes a giant o a man, compared to the clothes he wore. He was aye sittin humphed up.

He says, "Mither," he says, "you feed awa at your pigs, Jack's awa to push his fortune."

"Ah," she says, "feel Jack, dinnae gae 'wa noo, 'cause ye'll jist get lost, an ye ken ye've niver been past the gate o the place there aa your life, Jack. Jist bide far ye are."

So: "Ah, but mither," he says, "I'm gaun awa to push my fortune, an nothing 'll dee me but I'm gaun to push my fortune."

"No, no, Jack, awa an play wi yir doggie."

He says, "No, I'm gaun to push my fortune."

She says, "Weel, Jack, dinna wander awa." But Jack niver bothers, mither or nothing else—he hauds awa, whenever she turns her back. An . . . he opens the gate an walks oot—and whenever he opened that gate, he's in anither world. He didnae know where he wes, because he'd niver been oot o the fairmyard in his life. An he walks doon the road. So—if everything be true, this'll be nae lies—there were a crossroads, an on wan o the signposts, says: 'To the Land of Enchantment.' So Jack says, "Here's for it."

So he hauds doon the road to the Land of Enchantment onywey. And in the Land of Enchantment—I must tell ye this, because you'll understand what I tell yeze!—everything spoke: animals, birds, everything spoke. So he's comin on, an he's feelin gey hungry, Jack. He's a gey lump o a lad, an he liked his meat, and he was feelin hungry. So he says, "Lord, I weisht I asked my mither for a bannock or something to take on the road wi me, 'cause it's gey hungry, gaun awa."

He's comin on, an he looks—an did ye ever see a horse-troch, aa kin o grown wi moss?—an a lovely troch it wis, at the road side. An Jack says: "O, thank the Lord, I'll get a drink onywey, it'll quench the hunger for a bittie—ma thirst tae." So—there a wee robin sittin on the edge o the water—the edge o the troch, ye ken—so he bends doon his heid an takes a drink.

The robin says, "Hullo, Jack."

He says, "Lord, bi God, it's a bird speakin! Whit are ye speakin for," he says, "I never heard a bird speak in ma life."

"Oh," he says, "Jack, ye're in the Land of Enchantment—everything an everybody can speak."

"Oh, but"—he says—"nae a bird!" He says: "If I didnae see't wi my ain een, I wouldnae believe."

"Oh yes, Jack, I can talk."

He says, "Fit wey d'ye ken ma name?"

"Oh," he says, "Jack, we knew ye were comin—we'd been waitin on ye for twenty-one year, Jack."

"Lord, ye'd a gey wait, had ye no?"

But—he has a drink o water—he says, "Ye ken fit I could dae wi, birdie," he says, "I could dae wi a richt feed o meat."

"Oh, well, Jack," he says, "jist follae me."

So it trittles awa, doon the road a bit, an here's a lovely thackit cot at the roadside, an an old woman as if she'd the age o a hunder, an she's rockin back an forrit in an aul rockin chair. So she says, "Come in, Jack." She says, "Go in an get your supper, Jack."

So when Jack comes in, here's a lovely table set, an a plate o porridge an milk an some tea, an so on, cakes an biscuits—nae it, scones, an things like that—there wisna ony cakes at that time, scones was home-made fancy at that time onywey. An a lovely young girl. An she supplied the food, d'ye see?

So he sits doon, an has a plate o this porridge, an it tasted lovely, he never tasted anything finer in his life. (When ye're hungry, aathing tastes fine). An he had some tea—no, I'm gaun through my story: I made a mistake in that story . . . there were nae tea; it was home-brewed ale. . . . He'd a mug o this home-brewed ale, an some scones, oatcakes, things like that.

So she says, "Jack, would you like to lie down?"

An he says, "I wouldnae care," he says, "I'm feelin gey weary," he says, "an things, an I could dee wi a lie-doon."

She says, "Come up here, Jack." An she takes him up, an there the loveliest feather bed that ever you seen in your life, a richt bed. And so Jack jist lies doon, an sinks in, an faas quite asleep.

So he's lyin, but he waukens through the night, an he's lyin on a sheep-skin an three peats. He says, "My God, ma bed's changed quick! Lord," he says, "a queer bed." But he faas awa again—Jack didnae worry, he wis used to lyin in ashes onywey. He faas awa again, but he waukens in the mornin, an he's lying in this lovely bed again. He says, "My God, this is a queer country." He says, "It's jist nae like ma mither's place at aa."

But he jumps oot-ower his bed, an he gaes doon, an the breakfast's waitin for him again. So . . . the young girl says: "Go out, an my grand-mother'll give ye some advice, Jack. In the land you're in, all advice you can get, you take, Jack, 'cause you'll need it, see?"

So Jack says, "Aye, I aye tak advice, lassie." He says: "It's nae doin ony hairm."

So he gaes oot tae the door, he says, "Weel, Grannie, how are ye keepin?"

"Och," she says, "fine, Jack." She says, "Jack, I'm gaun to give ye some advice. When you go along this road today, Jack, never talk to anybody first. Wait tae they talk to you first."

He says: "Weel, whatever ye say, Grannie."

So he says good-bye, he hauds on his wey, but when he's gone . . . doon a bit o the road, the young girl cries efter him, an gies him some sang-wiches to carry on with—ye ken, scones an butter, an things like that. So he carries them wi him, ye see?

But, to mak a lang story short an a short story lang, he hauds on the road. An he's ho the road, hey the road, doon this road, ye see? But he's walkin, an he hears the bells o a village, like a church-bell ringin awa; it wis helluva sweet-like music, ye ken—he hears awa in a hollow, ye wad think; it wis bonny-like. So he comes on ower the ridge, an he looks doon in a den, an here's a lovely village. So, . . . the most of the scones . . . that he got, he ate them, and there was a small bit o . . . a somethin got up in a piece o cloth, ye ken—an he opens it up, an here's a gold piece. Either a geeny, or a . . . what kin it was I dinna ken, but a gold piece, that's aa that I ken. An he takes it oot, looks at it, pits it in his pocket, an gaes on tae the village.

So he looks, an here's a inn. He says, "I'll gang in here," he says, "for some home-brewed ale an scones," he says (he wes feelin hungry again). So he gaes in, an he orders home-brewed ale an scones, an he eats a gey hillock, at least a platefae. An has a richt drink.

So he looks ower in a corner, an there three men playin cards, an they're aa playin cards jist, neither speakin, movin, or anything else, jist playin cards. An there a man dressed fae the paws o his taes tae the heid . . . his heid in green. An oh . . . a very cunnin-lookin man—mebbe he's a man aboot fifty, but what a cunnin face. Jist by the face, ye would ken he was very clever—that man had brains.

So Jack gings ower til 'im an says, "Can I get a game?"

He says, "Have ye money?"

Jack says, "Weel, I hinna a lot o money, but I've money" (he had change o this gold piece). An he says, "I'd like a game."

He says, "Can you play at cards? We don't play," he says, "with men that cannot play at cards."

"Oh," he says, "I've practised a bittie in my day"—twenty-one year he'd practised—he says, "I've practised a bittie o it in my day," but he sits doon, an he starts to play at cards. An the four of them plays an plays—but Jack . . . the Green Man o Knowledge wis a good card-player, but he couldnae beat Jack, 'cause Jack had aa his life played wi his collie. He could play cards!

But aathing's comin Jack's wey, so the ither two faas oot, but Jack an the Green Man of Knowledge plays an plays an plays up tae the early 'oors o the mornin.

Sae he looks at him, an he says, "Jack," he says, "ye're maybe yir mother's feel," he says, "but ye're too good a man for me at cards." He says, "Good-bye, Jack."

14

He says, "Wait a minute. Fa are ye?"

He says, "I'm the Green Man o Knowledge."

"Sae you're the Green Man o Knowledge?"

"Aye."

He says, "Far dae ye bide?"

He says, "East o the moon and west o the stars."

He says, "Lord, that's a queer direction."

He says, "Make oot o't onythin ye like, Jack." Sae he jist left like that.

He jist gied a kin of laugh: "My God, he's a gey peculiar kin o lad. Och," he says, "a lad winna worry. I've got plenty o money now."

But he heaps aa his . . . he has any amount o money, I couldnae value it, but he's any amount. So he pits it in bags, an he says tae the innkeeper, he says, "Will ye keep this gold to me till I come back this wey?" he says. "I must fin' far the Green Man o Knowledge bides."

An the innkeeper shaks his head. He says, "Jack, dinnae follae him," he says. He says, "You'll go to disaster if you follae him."

"Ach," Jack says, "aabody has only oncet to die—why worry! I'll just follae him." But Jack reckoned withoot the Green Man o Knowledge.

So he hauds on the road, the only road to walk oot o the village, in the opposite direction fra whence he come.

An he's haudin on the road, ye ken—an he started gettin tired an weary again, an he took a few gold pieces wi him, nae much, in his pocket, 'fear he would come tae ony mair inns or that, ye ken, where he could get refreshments an that. An he's haudin on the road—but he jist comes right in aboot til anither thackit hoosie, the same.

He says, "Well, I'll go up an see this thackit hoosie," he says, "an they might help me onywey. I'll pay them."

So he chaps at the door, so . . . he hears a voice: "Come in, Jack."

He says, "Lord, they're weel-informed in this country," he says, "everybody kens my name." So he opens the door an comes in, an says, "I'm in."

She says, "Are ye hungry, Jack? I suppose you are."

He says, "Yes, I'm hungry."

She says, "Sit down, Jack."

So he sits doon. So he gets the same meal again as he got in the ither place. An yon girl. . . . If the first girl was bonnie, this girl was ten times bonnier. She was much bonnier. And if the auld woman was old, this

15

woman was much older—she was ancient! And she was sittin, rockin awa in her chair tae. So they pits him to bed, but the same thing happens in the bed I tellt ye in the other part o the story. He goes tae his bed an rises in the mornin, and the peats was through the night. . . . But he notices before he goes to bed this old woman was knittin and she was knittin just a round piece of knittin, ye ken, like crochetin, but it was knittin she wis, jist a round piece like that table there. And it was lyin on the floor when he cam in the mornin.

"Now," she says, "Jack, you're lookin for the Green Man o Knowledge." He says, "I am."

And she says, "Jack, we're here to help you, because you could never manage yourself, Jack."

He says, "Weel," he says, "I'll tak aa the help I can get."

So efter his breakfast, she says, "Jack," she says, "take this piece of knittin out to the door, and lay it down and sit on't—and sit plait-leggèd, Jack, and cross your arms, and," she says, "whatever happens, don't look behind you." She says, "Don't look behind you, because if you look behind you, it's the end." She says, "Whatever happens, don't look behind you."

So he sits this plait-leggèd, and folds his arms. And she says, "Say 'Away with you.' And," she says, "whirl it three times round, when you land with it," she says, "and say 'Home with you'. And," she says, "that'll be all right, Jack."

And he says, "Weel, weel, thank ye."

So he says, "Away with you"—but he moves that quick the wind just leaves his body. And he's through what he doesn't know what—Hell-fire, brimstone, water, everything. And he's just dying to look back! But he minds—he's a strong-willpowered man—he minds what the auld woman said. He says, "Weel, she did nae hairm so far," he says. "We'll just keep lookin forrit." So he looks forrit.

But he lands, and he was glaid to land. So he stands up, and he catches this bit o knittin, and he pits it roond his heid three times like that, ye ken, an he says, "Away with ye"—or "Back with ye", it wis, sure, and away it wis. So he jist comes roond the corner, he hears "ting-ting-ting", a blacksmith on an anvil, tinkerin, an so he comes in-aboot, and here a house. And here an old woman sittin like the first, rockin, ye ken, and she was older. If age coonts in that country, she was older.

And he says, "Ah well, well"—he goes in-aboot, and she says, "Well, Jack, we've been waitin for you." She says, "Go in to the house, Jack." So Jack goes into the house, and he gets the same meal again. The same bed, the same procedure aa through, till the mornin.

"Now," she says, "Jack, go round to the smiddy shop," she says, "and you shall see," she says, "my husband, and he's made something for you, Jack. And . . . do what he told you, and you won't go wrong."

So the smith says, "I want to talk to you, Jack," he says. "Now," he says, "you're nearin the Green Man o Knowledge. But," he says, "the Green Man o Knowledge has many precautions." ([I'm] forgetting aboot them.) He says, "There must be a river to cross—there a river to be crossed," he says. He says, "I can't help you cross it, Jack, and there a bridge. But," he says, "if you step on that bridge it'll turn to a spider's web. You'll fall through it, Jack." He says, "If you fall in the water, Jack, you're finished, because the water goes into boilin lava." He says, "You're instantly dead." He says, "There only one way across, Jack," he says, "it's his youngest daughter. He's got three daughters, Jack, and the youngest one," he says, "is the most powerful of the lot." He says, "They come down to swim, Jack, every mornin," he says, "at mebbe ten o'clock," he says, "that time o the mornin. And," he says, "whenever they touch water," he says, "they turn to swans." He says, "There two black swans, Jack, and a white swan. It's the white swan you must get, Jack. But if you don't trap her in the way I'm tellin you, Jack, you're finished, for she'll pull you doon. You watch where they're puttin their clothes, and pick every article up o her clothes—and if you leave a hairpin, she'll make a outfit out o it," he says, "don't leave nothin." And he says, "Jack, they cross the bridge to the side you're on," he says, "and go into the water," he says, "from that side, Jack." He says, "They come back and dress there, Jack."

So he says, "Weel, it'll likely be true. But," he says, "this is a gey queer affair, but," he says, "weel, weel, we'll try 't."

He says, "You see that horse-shoe, Jack?" It was a very large horse-shoe. He says, "You sit on the horse-shoe, Jack, and don't look behind, whatever you do, and say, 'Away wi you!' and," he says, "put it round your head three times and say, 'Back wi you!'"

So Jack does't, and he gings through the same again, it wis jist torture. But he lands at the banks o the river. And now, as the blacksmith telt him

17

to hide hissel, so Jack hides hissel . . . just aside the bridge, and he sees this three lovely maidens comin ower, and they were bonnie lassies. But the littlest one was the slenderest, and the most graceful o the lot, you would have thought, you know? So they come trippin ower the bridge and undress, and into the water. And whenever they touch the water, the two oldest ones turned til a black swan, and they swum fast an away. And this youngest one undresses; and he watches where she pits her clothes, and ye ken what like Jack, I mean a fairm servant, never seen a woman in his life hardly, says, "Lord, this is fine!" They're into the water, and they're away swimming. So he's awa up wi her claes, up every stitch o claes she had, everything, even the very ribbons, and hides them.

So the two oldest ones comes out and dresses, and across the bridge and away. And she's up and doon this side, and she says, "Where are you, Jack?"

He says, "I'm here."

She says, "My clothes, please, Jack."

"Ah na na, I'm nae giein ye nae claes," he says. "I was weel warned aboot ye."

She says, "Jack, please, my clothes. Are you a gentleman?"

"Na na," he says, "I'm just Jack the Feel. I'm nae gentleman."

She says, "What have I to do, Jack?"

He says, "Well," he says. He says, "It's a cruel thing to ask, but," he says, "you must help me across this river on your back."

She says, "Oh Jack, you'd break my slender back."

"Ah," he says, "the old smith's nae feel. Ye're nae sae slender." He says, "Ye'll take me across the river."

She says, "Well Jack, step on my back, but whatever you do, on the peril of my life and your life, don't tell how ye got across."

He says, "Okay."

So he jumps on her back, and she takes him across, an he steps up on the bank.

So . . . "Now," she says, "Jack, he shall try his best and . . . [to ken] how ye got across, but tell him nothing."

He says, "Weel, weel," he says, "I'll tell him nothing."

So he walks up to the hoose—noo she gaes awa an gets dressed, an runs past him awa—he jist goes straight up tae the hoose an he chaps at

18

the door, see. So the door opens, and here's the Green Man o Knowledge, and he was flabbergasted . . . he was shocked!

So he looks at him an he says, "My God, Jack, how did you get here?"

"Och, jist the wey ye get."

He says, "Jack, how did you cross the river?"

"Och, flew across."

He says, "You've no wings, Jack."

"Oh, nothing's impossible. I can grow wings," he says.

"Well, Jack, come in," he says. He says, "I must shake your hand," he says. "You're a good man." So Jack shakes his hand—and Jack's against the waa—sae he gies Jack a push, an Jack's through a kin o drap-door affair, an he lands in a wee roomie, an there's nae so much room for a moose, never mind a big man like Jack, he gies a couple of notes.

An he looks, an there a bit dry breid, an hit blue-moulded, an water, an it says, "Drink, an eat, an be merry." He says, "My God, a lad widnae be very merry on that!"

So he's sittin awa, but 'at night he hears a whisper—here's this girl that helped him. She says, "Jack, you've won me." She says, "Whenever you made me take you across the river," she says, "you spelled me, an I love you," she says. "I'll love you till the day I die, an I can't do nothing else." But she says, "I'll help you anyway, but please, Jack, don't move foolish, 'cause he'll kill ye." She says, "My father, he's evil."

She says, "Here's some food, Jack." So Jack gets a feed o meat, an he was one aboot loves the meat! . . . He was sittin there fair right wi hunger aboot.

So in the mornin, the place opens and Jack creeps oot. An the Green Man o Knowledge says, "How was ye last night, Jack?"

"Ach," Jack says, "very comfortable, jist fine."

He says, "Ye wisnae fine, Jack?"

"A never slept better."

He says, "You're not bad to please, Jack."

"Ach, a lad cannae be bad to please in this times."

So he says, "Would you like," he says, "Jack," he says, "would you like," he says, "to prove to me that you are a man?"

Jack says, "Yes, I would like to prove to ye I'm a man."

"Well," he says, "Jack, I'll gie ye three tasks." He says, "They're not hard tasks, any child could do them," he says. He says, "They're not hard tasks, but," he says, "they take doin, Jack." He says, "Do you see," he says, "that dry wal . . . well in the garden, Jack?"

He says, "Ay, I see the dry wal."

He says, "I want you," he says, "Jack, to go down to the bottom o that wal," he says, "an take out my wife's engagement ring," he says, "which she lost there twenty year ago. Oh," he says, "it isn't hard to dae, Jack, I could do it."

Jack says, "Why d'ye nae dee it?"

He says, "I want you to do it, Jack."

Jack says, "Weel, I'll try 't." So he's claain his heid, an, "My God!"

An he says, "Jack, not today; tomorrow, Jack." An he says, "Come on tae I show you a photograph o my wife, Jack." So Jack's standin lookin—he says, "Aye, she's a bonnie woman"—an he gies a push again, an he's intae anither kin o a cavity, an he gied a note this time.

So the hard breid's there again, an the water, an the same fare.

So here she comes again, wi mair food for 'im. So she says, "Jack, the task he's going to give you is near impossible—it *is* impossible, Jack," she says. "I shall help you to make it possible. Now," she says, "the well is thirty-five feet [deep] Jack. An," she says, "I'll make a lether . . . a ladder with my body from the tap o the well tae the bottom o the well." An she says, "If you miss wan step, Jack, you'll break a bone in my body." An she says, "For God's sake, Jack, watch what you're doin."

So Jack says, "Weel. . . ." An he says, "Whit wey will I see't?"

She says, . . . "The well's covered in mud," she says, "it's a terrible well, but I'll make the bottom clear, an you'll see the ring shinin."

He says, "Weel, weel, I'll try that."

So he comes to the wal: the Green Man o Knowledge takes him oot the next mornin, takes him to the wal—an says: "There's the well, Jack."

So Jack says, "Well." So Jack leans ower, and feels for the lether, an he feels her there, her shouthers, God!—an he takes one step . . . away in plunge doon quick, kiddin he's drappin like, an he's steppin doon, steppin doon, till he comes tae the last step, an he misses—he says, "My God, I've broke her neck! . . . Ah," he says, "weel, weel, we cannae help it," so he grabs the ring, an he's hup like the haimmers o hell, an oot o the wal.

An . . . so he shows the Green Man o Knowledge it, like that. He says, "There's the ring."

"Oh," he says, "you're clever, Jack." He says, "Let me see 't, Jack."

"No," Jack says. "That's not you who done the work."

He says, "Who's helpin you, Jack?"

He says, "Nobody's helpin me."

He says, "Somebody's helpin you, Jack."

Jack says, "No!"

He says, "Well, Jack," he says, "you're a clever man," he says. "You've deen the first task," he says, "but," he says, "the second one's harder, Jack."

So he takes Jack back, an Jack he sits down to a lovely meal. But Jack's away to eat his meal when the seat gaes oot ablow him an whump! away in another cavity. He says, "My God, I canna stand this much longer," he says, "it'll kill me."

But he's sittin, an he's lookin at this hard breid again, when she comes again. "Oh," she says, "Jack," she says, "if it had been the other step, ye'd have broke my neck." She says, "You broke my pinkie, Jack, and I wore dinner gloves and Father didn't notice it." She says, "If he had noticed it, Jack, we'd both have been dead."

He says, "Fit dis he plan to dee to me the morn?"

She says, "He's got a task for ye to do, Jack. Ye've to build a castle out of pure nothing within sixty minutes."

"Oot o nothing?" he says, "Lord, I couldnae thack a hoose in three months," he says, "never mind build a castle oot o nothing."

She says, "Jack," she says, "he's goin to take ye tae a hill at the back of our castle, an ask ye to build it. And," she says, "it must be bigger and larger and nicer than ours. An," she says, "Jack, I shall do it. But," she says, "watch what ye're sayin, Jack, 'cause ye'll get the baith o us trapped." See?

He says, "Weel, weel," but he gets oot next mornin again, an the Green Man o Knowledge says: "How was ye last night, Jack?"

"Ah," he says, "I wis niver better." He says, "My God, ye've got richt places in this hoose. I like this hoose—this castle."

So he says, "Yes, Jack," he says, "I've a small task for ye today, Jack. Anybody could do it, but," he says, "I want you to do it, Jack."

21

Jack says, "What is 't?"

He says, "I want ye to build a castle, Jack, bigger than my one and larger, and nicer in every way." He says, "I want ye to build it in sixty minutes."

Jack says, "That's a gey stiff task to gie a lad."

"Oh, but you're Jack," he says, "you got here," he says, "you got the engagement ring, Jack, this shouldn't bother you."

"Well," Jack says, "I'll try't."

He says, "Go on, Jack, do't."

"Ah but," Jack says, "I'll be giein awa trade secrets—you go awa," he says.

So he says, "I cannot watch, Jack?"

"No," Jack says, "I canna let ye watch." So he turns his back and leaves.

So Jack sits for aboot half-an-'oor, an he says, "If this deem disnae hurry up, I'll be clean killed. This lad'll be back here because she's takin an aafae time. . . . Oh," he says. "My God, this is nae ees, she's takin too lang." He says, "I'll be makin tracks oot o here." So he turns roon, an the castle's at the back o'm, he wis lyin lookin the ither wey! So he says, "Thank God."

But he's walkin roon it, an he's lookin ower it—an there a hole aboot the size o this hoose. He says, "Oh," he says, "she's made a mistake. Oh," he says, "Whar is she?"

An he hears a voice sayin, "Jack, that's nae a mistake. When he comes an looks at this hole, Jack, he'll say, 'What's this, what's this?' An . . . you say til him, Jack, . . . 'I've left that part for you to full up', an see whit he says, Jack."

So up comes the Green Man o Knowledge, an he says, "My goodness, whit a lovely castle," he says, "Jack," he says, "I do gie ye credit," He says, "You are a clever man." So he walks aa roon' it, an he says, "Oh my goodness, Jack! Whit a mess! What did ye leave this hole here for?"

He says, "That's for you to fill."

He says, "Jack, who's helpin ye?"

Jack says, "Na, na, naebody's helpin me. I wis only once pals wi a collie dog," he says, "that's aa."

So he says, "Well, well, Jack."

But the third task . . . ye ken, I canna exactly mind. . . . Oh yes, the third task was to clear the ants in a wood—ay, he'd tae clear every one oot in the half an 'oor. An . . . ye know ants, there millions o it, they're uncoontable, ye can't clean ants. So . . . he takes Jack out next mornin, the same proceedins again . . . an he says: "Ye've got to clean all this ants, Jack, I'll give ye half an hour. If you can do that, Jack, I'll give you as much money as you can carry, any o my daughters for your wife, and your freedom, Jack, an," he says, "my castle, if ye need it—if ye want it—I'll gie ye your freedom."

"Well," Jack says, "freedom means a lot to me. I've an auld mither," he says, "at hame," he says. "She's workin with the pigs, and," he says, "I'd like to help her tae." But Jack looks at this wuid, an he says, "My God, this'll take some clearin." But of coorse, she did the job for him again.

So he says, "Jack, you are clever. Now," he says, "Jack, come to my house," he says, and he gives Jack a lovely meal this time, an no tricks. "Now," he says, "Jack," he says, "I've got you," he says, "four bags of gold here," he says, "an in each bag, the money's near uncoontable(?)," he says, "and," he says, "you're past bein a rich man," he says, "Jack. You're very wealthy," he says. An he says, "I'll take you to the stable," he says, "and gie ye the pick of my . . . my horses . . . I keep all mares," he says, "and they are lovely horses, Jack." An he says, "You can have whatever horse you want."

So Jack says, "Weel, weel," he says.

But Jack's pickin his gold (an the Green Man o Knowledge is walkin along in front o him), when he hears the voice o the girl again, sayin, "Jack, take the old mule—Jack, take the old mule."

So he says, "Well, well," he says.

So he gaes intae the stable, an he's stan'in, ye see, an he's lookin—an they were lovely beasts, oh, there nae doot aboot them, loveliest beasts that he'd seen. There a grey meer, an he could see the fire in her eyes— fit a lovely meer. An there anither meer, this clean black meer, an he could see the fire in her eyes. So Jack looks at them, and he looks at this wee scruffy-lookin animal o a mule, an he says, "My goodness, fit 'm I gaunna dae wi that?" He says, "My God, she hisnae been wrang yet," tae hissel. "I better take a tellin." He says, "My God, it's a sin to throw this gold oot-ower the back o it." An he looks at this meers . . . he says to the Green Man o Knowledge, "I'd like that wee dunkey, it's fast enough for Jack."

23

The Green Man of Knowledge

"Oh, my goodness, Jack," he says, "you wouldn't take *that?*" . . . He says, "It would disgrace ye goin through the country, Jack."

"Ach," Jack says, "I'm nae good tae disgrace, I'm nae worriet. I'll take that wee mule."

"No, no, Jack," he says, "I wouldn't allow ye to take that, ye'll take one of this mares."

So Jack's newsin awa, an he straps his gold on tap o the mule's back. An he's newsin awa, an the wee mule's stan'in wi nae rein or nothing else, so he's ower his leg, an it wis nae bother, 'cause it wis only a wee thingie, just draps ower its back and he's away, an he's aff his mark an this wee mule could rin. 'Is wee donkey or mule or whatever it wis, but it's rinnin, an Jack says, "My God, take it easy, lassie, nothing'll catch ye."

She says, "Jack, you don't know my people," she says, "they shall catch me if I don't hurry, Jack."

"Aw, Lord, lassie, they'll never see ye—take your time, deemie, ye'll jist kill yersel hastin."

She says, "No, Jack, I must run, and run hard."

Jack says, "Take your . . . but, God," he says, "hurry up, there he's ahin us." An here, they're jist at the back o his neck. An he says, "Run harder."

So she's rinnin, but she says, "Jack, I haven't got the speed for him." She says, "Jack, look in my left ear," she says, "an you shall see a drop of water," she says. "Throw it over your shoulder, an ask for rivers, lakes and seas behint you, and a clear road in front o you."

So he throws it ower his shouther; he says, "Gie's lakes, seas, and . . . so on, behint me, but," he says, "give me a clear road in front o me." An he looks behind—"Aw," he says, "lassie, take your breath, there's nothing but seas, they'll never get through it," he says, "they'll be droon't."

She says, "Jack, you don't know my people." She's rinnin harder, see? And . . . no, I was gone through my story. This meers wis her sisters, changed into meers and if you killed them, it didna mean you wouldna have to kill them necessarily again.

So he says, "Ah, ye're safe enough, lassie, jist take your time."

She says, "No, Jack." An he looks ahin him, and they're ahin him again, an the Green Man of Knowledge on tap o one o their backs, one o his daughters' backs, and they're rinnin.

So she says, "Look in my left ear, Jack, an ye'll see a spark . . . a stone."

24

She says, "Throw it over your shoulder, Jack, an wish for mountains, hills and dales behind you, and a clear road in front of you." So he does the same again, and the same happens, so he jist tells her to take her time again, but na, she winnae listen, she jist keeps batterin on. But as sure as truth, they're just ahin him again, within any time.

So she says, "Jack," she says, "I love you, and," she says, "I will destroy my people for you. But," she says, "Jack, it shall put a spell on me for a year, an you too. An," she says, . . . "look in my left ear an ye'll see a spark o fire." She says, "Throw it behind you, an ask for fire, hell an pits behind you, an a clear road in front of you."

So he did this, an he looks roond, and he sees her people witherin in the fire, an dyin, see? Whatever happened aboot it, he seen them jist witherin awa in the fire.

So she turned intil a woman again, and he . . . jist stands on his feet . . . haudin his gold in his hands. And she says, "Jack," she says, "now, because of that," she says, "I must leave ye for a year." She says, "One year from today I'll come for ye."

"Ah," he says, "lassie, I'll be waiting."

She says, "Jack, let nobody kiss you." She says, "If your mother kisses you," she says, "if anybody kisses you," she says, "ye'll forget the whole affair, Jack, forget the whole proceedings. You'll remember nothing aboot where you've been or what you've done." She says, "Jack, don't let nobody kiss ye."

So he says, "Weel, weel, I'll let naebody kiss me if it's that important, but," he says, "I'll see ye fin ye come onywey." He wisna gaun to worry 'cause he'd plenty o money.

So he hauds awa hame, "God Almichty," he says, "I'm nae far fae hame—that's my mither's place doon there." So he's ower the palins, an here's his auld wife's place.

"O," she says, "Jack, my peer loon," an she's trying to kiss Jack.

"Na, na, mither, I want nae kissin an slaverin," he says, "I want naething to dee wi that. No, no, stop it." So he would hae nae kissin. But he went intae the hoose, an here's his big collie dog, an his collie dog jumps up on his chest and gies him a big lick. That wis hit, in the instant he forgot aathing.

So Jack's plenty money, an he's . . . nae 'Feel Jack' now. He's 'Sir Jack', an this, an that—money maks aa the difference. It even maks feels gentlemen. But . . .

So Jack's bocht a big place, and he's working awa within twa-three months, an the miller's dochter's a gey wenchy deem, an he throws an eye at the miller's dochter, see, an him an the miller's dochter's engaged to get mairriet. So Jack's a business man, he's aye intae business, an gettin a lot o payin work, an that; he mebbe couldnae write his name, but he jist put his cross, an worked awa wi't like that, ye ken.

But . . . So, he wis jist gettin mairriet, a year tae the day he cam hame. So . . . the nicht o his weddin, Jack's aafae busy, an there aa the guests there, but Jack's, ye ken, aafae busy—wi his papers an things like that, I suppose, an he's in his room. So a poor tattered and torn girl—but a bonnie quyne—comes tae the back door, and asks for a job, see? So they says, "Whit can ye dee?"

She says, "I can cook, I can clean," She says, "I would like"—

An he says, "Oh, I'll take you on at the weddin, tonight. Help us to cook an clean an aathing, and for a couple o days efter the weddin, and then ye'll have to go."

She says, "Yes, that'll do me fine, thank you."

So she's washin dishes, an scrubbin awa, ye ken, an they're waitin on the preacher—but the preacher's takin a gey while, 'cause he was comin on horse-back at that time, ye see, an it was a gey bit fae the . . . fae a village—an the preacher's takin a good while. An they're gettin aa impatient, the guests, ye ken; they're gettin—did ye ever see . . . gettin uncomfortable sittin—and they're aa walkin aboot newsin.

So she says, "I believe I could smooth the guests a little, an pass away the time for them, because I can do a trick," she says. "I have a wooden hen and a wooden cock, and they can talk, they can pick, and," she says, "everything."

"Oh," they says, "that's great, we'll hear it."

So she goes ben, an ye can imagine her amongst aa this well-dressed folk wi a, mebbe an aul white torn skirt on her, gey ragged lookin an things, amongst aa this well-dressed kin o folk. An she's doon this two birds, a cock an a hen. So she scattered some corn, but Jack jist comes oot to watch yin tee, ye see. But Jack's stan'in watchin and the cock picks an looks at her, an the hen picks an looks at the cock, and the hen says to the cock, "Do you remember me, Jack?"

An the cock looks an says, "Remember you? No, I couldn't say I do remember you." So the cock gaes on pickin.

She says, "Jack, do you remember the Green Man of Knowledge?"

"The Green Man of Knowledge? Oh no, I don't remember him." So the cock gaes on pickin.

She says, "Jack, do you remember me, the woman you love?"

He says, "Ah . . . no, I'm sorry, I don't know you."

She says, "Jack, do you remember when I killed my own people for you, Jack?"

An the cock looked an he says, "Yes, I do remember you."

An Jack says, "It's you, deem! It's you, lassie, is't?" He's aye recollected the deem. So the weddin wis cancelled, and he mairriet her, an they lived happily ever after.

That's the end o my story. But there a gey lot o cuttin done, ye ken, or I'd never managed to tell it aa—in twa nichts!

The King and the Miller

John Stewart

A'm tellin ye a little story aboot a miller an his daughter: he hed one o the nicest daughters could be seen in the country, an everybody hed a fancy of her. And the keeng—the young king was livin not very far from her an he hed a notion of her, an he didnae know what way for tae gain this girl. An he went doon tae the mill one day, and he said, "A'm goin to gie ye three questions," he says, "miller, an ye know," he says, "the keeng's word's never broke. And if ye don't answer me that three questions," he says, "your head will go on my gate."

"Well," says the miller, "if A can answer them A'll try ma best."

He says, "Ye know," he says, "that I can do what I like," he says, "I'm keeng o this country, an my word'll stand."

"Very well," says the miller, he says, "what is it?"

"Well," he says, "you must tell me," he says, "the weight o the moon. That's wan. You must tell me," he says, "hoo many stars is in the heavens. That's two. An you must—third one," he says, "you must tell me what A'm thinkin on."

"Oh well," says the miller, he says, "A doot my heid'll go on yir gates."

An he says, "Gin this time a year an a day," he says, "A'll be doon," he says, "an ask ye the questions. An if ye're not right," he says, "yir head comes off."

So this poor miller now, he's gaun up an doon, thinkin tae himsel what could he say or what could he do. An there's a young shepherd lad not very far away, and he was helpin him at the hairvest, takin in the hairvest. An . . . the shepherd chap says tae him, "Gosh bless me, miller," he says, "what's ado wi ye? Ye're aafae dour be when I cam here first."

"Yes," he says, "laddie, A'm dour. An if you kent," he says, "what I ken," he said, "you would be dour too."

He says, "What is it?"

28

The King and the Miller

So he told the shepherd what he wis told be the keeng, An he says, "You know the keeng's word," he says, "goes far."

"Oh well," he says, "A'll tell you one thing," he says, "miller," he says: "if you promise me tae get your daughter," he says, "as a wife," he says, "A'll clear ye o that."

"Well," he says, "A can't give her," he says, "unless she's willin." An he goes in tae his daughter an he asks her a question; he says, "My daughter," he says, "ye know," he says, "what I've tae suffer."

She said, "Yes."

He says, "Would you get my life saved," he says, "fir tae mairry a man?"

She says, "A wid mairry," she says, "the day, if it wid save yir life."

"Well," he says, "there a man'll save my life if ye marry him."

"Who is he?" she says.

He says, "So an so's shepherd."

"Well," she says, "he's as good as what I am. A'll marry him if he'll save yir life, but not, faither, till yir life's saved."

"A'll bet yez he'll save my life—I think."

So the shepherd an them agreed that he would save his life. So that day year—it's a Hogmanay night—he was up the side o the dam an who did he meet but this young keeng. A should have said that the shepherd dressed himsel up with a white baerd an put on the miller's suit o clothes on him, and he's away up beside the dam fir tae meet the keeng: this was the night he wis tae meet him an answer his questions. So—

"Good evenin, miller."

"Good evenin, ma noble keeng," he said.

"Did you answer my questions?"

"Oh well," he says, "so far as I think," he says, "A hiv."

He says, "What weight is the moon?"

He says, "The moon'll be a hundredweight. There's four quaarters in the moon," he says, "an there four quarters in a hundredweight."

He says, "That's very good! Can ye tell me hoo mony stars," he says, "as shines in the heavens?"

"Oh, there'll be aboot seven million, five hundred an fifty-five, an if ye dinnae believe me ye can coont them yirsel."

"A cannae—I cannae coont them," . . . says the keeng. He says, "Ye cannae tell me," he says, "what . . . A'm thinkin on. This one'll . . . puzzle ye," he says.

"Yes," he says, "A can. You think," he says, "ye're speakin tae the auld miller, but ye'll fin' it's his son-in-laa ye're talkin to!"

So the young fella got the auld man saved an married the girl. So that's the end o ma story.

The Three Dogs

Bella Higgins

Oncet in times—it wisn't in your time nor yet in my time, but it wis in someone's time, very very many many years ago—there wis a brother an sister lived away in the top o the glen. They had a small croft and the brother an the sister worked it between them. But one day the brother was away out in the fields workin, when a packman came by an he calls in tae see his sister, wantin her to buy something. However, time rolls by, but this young man's sister she gave birth to a son, which—the packman was the father.

But hooever, A'll have to leave that now an go on to John. That year was pretty hard, the weren't much money to be made. So he says, "A'll have tae take wan ae the cows in," he says, "an try an sell it to raise the price o the rent."

"Well," she says, "you'll have to try an get a good penny for them, because you know we have nothing; times is pretty hard on us," she says, "an we've nothing." She says, "Just go to the market an try an get the highest ye can get for it."

So he cleans his beast an he toddles on the road. He comes to cross roads. Here he sees a man stannin with a dog.

"Good mornin, John," he says.

"Good mornin, sir," he says. "It's a fine mornin."

"It is that," he says. "Where are ye goin, John?"

"Well," he says, "A'm forced tae take the cow," he says, "tae sell it to pay ma rent."

"Ha," he says, "it's no a bad-lookin cow."

"It is not," he says. "A good milkin cow."

He says, "How can me an you have a swap?"

"What," he says, "hiv a swap?"

"Yes, John," he says, "ye'll never regret it," he says, "for this is one o the cleverest dogs," he says, "that ever was pupped, an the wisest."

31

"Ho," he says, "A believe that. But," he says, "if I wis to . . . take the dog fir ma cow," he says, "I mightnae go home," he says, "fir my sister would kill me. She would jist meet me at the door," he says, "with a brush in her hand, an," he says, "jist give me it ower the heid," he says. "I mightnae go home."

"Ah but," he says, "once she kens—begins to know the dog," he says, "she'll be very well pleased at it." He says, "This is Swift, and," he says, "there never wis a hare," he says, "or a rabbit ever took the hills but Swift could catch."

"Ha well," he says, "ye're temptin me, laddie," he says, "an I jist think A will have it, for," he says, "A'm aafa fond of a good rabbit dog."

"Ah well," he says, "ye'll get plenty o rabbits afore you go home yet, John."

"Very good," he says, "an here's yir cow," he says, "an good luck tae ye."

So he gets the dog an he's comin home an he jist met his sister at the door: she says, "Wis ye at the market a'ready?"

"No," he says, "A wisnae at the market."

"An where did ye get the dog?"

"Oh," says he, "A had a swap," he says, "wi a man 'at had the dog," he says, "an he says it's the swiftest dog in the world, there nothing tae baet it," he says, "as swift's his name. An," he says, "dinnae you worry," he says, "A'll hae plenty o rabbits an hares; we'll no stairve."

Oh, she near aboot killed him wi pokers an tangs an everything she got in her hand, she near killed him.

"Well," he says, "it cannae be helped, but," he says, "the bargain's made."

"No, wait," she says, "you know," she says, "there only another two days o the market to be held, an you take the other cow," she says, "an if ye'd swap again fir a dog," she says, "ye neednae come back, for ye'll be killed," she says. "A'll roast ye."

But hooever he sets off again wi his cow, an here he meets the same auld man, an he has another dog.

"Man," he says, "John," he says, "that's a braa cow ye have. Ye're goin to the market the day."

"Aye," he says, "but dinnae speak tae me aboot swappin," he says, "nae mair, for," he says, "I was near killed," he says; "ma bones is sore yet with the lickin I got fae my sister."

"Ha, but John," he says, "never mind that. This is a dog," he says, "this is Able. Man," he says, "or if a rabbit or a hare," he says, "goes intae a dyke," he says, "he can jist knock it down," he says, "an when it springs to run," he says, "Swift can catch it. An," he says, "you'll be a rich man yet through your three dogs."

"Oh well," he says, "A stood a baetin," he says, "'at would kill a horse a'ready, an," he says, "A'll stand another one fir the dog."

So he swaps again, gets the dog an he gies this auld man his cow. He's comin whistlin back again, an she jist eyes the dog. She never asked him no questions, she jist goes in for anything she can get in her hand, an his eyes is black an blue with skelps wi pokers an tongs an bizoms and shuffels, everything she could get in her hand she would let him have it.

But hooever, "Now," she says, "ye've only the morra to go wi the cow," she says, "or if ye don't have a deal tomorra," she says, "ye neednae return here."

But hooever, makin a long story short—we'll need tae cut it short—away he goes again with the third cow. Here he meets the same man. An his eyes is blue an he could hardly speak, his lips is all swollen an his nose is aa swollen, an he's, oh, he's a picture to look at.

"Oh," he says, "dinnae talk to me," he says, "aboot another dog," he says. "I was near murder't last night."

"Ha, wheesht, John," he says. "Ye can stand another hammerin ower the heid o this dog," he says. "This is what they call," he says—"ye've Swift and ye've Able," he says: "this is Knowall. Knowall," he says, "knows where every rabbit or beast," he says, "lies. It has a scent," he says, "can jist take the other two til it." He says, "Able," he says, "can knock down any wall or dyke," he says, "an Swift can catch them," he says. "Ye've got the three dogs, an mind ye," he says, "John, they'll be worth money tae ye yet. An," he says, "A'm tellin ye, ye're lossin yir chance now," he says, "an when ye stood," he says, "two rows an two batterins ye can stand a third one."

"Oh well," he says, "here ye go," he says. "I dinnae mind," he says, "what wey she hits me an batters me," he says, "A'll stand it, fir the sake of the dogs."

33

So whatever, he comes home wi his dog, and that's the three dogs he has now: Swift, Knowall and Able. Oh, when she met him she near—ye talk about a lickin an a hammerin: she near aboot massacreed him. "Out ye go," she says, "ye're not to be here," an she drove the three dogs away. "Go on," she says, "wi yir three dogs out o this; don't enter my door." So the three o them went out.

But they went away for a day's huntin; a day's huntin. Knowall says, "Jaik?"

"What," he says, "can ye speak?"

"Oh yes," says the dog, he says, "A can speak." He says, "There's an old packman in wi yir sister," he says, "in the house. And," he says, "he's been carryin on," he says, "an correspondin wi yir sister," he says, "for many years. And she's going tae keep him all night. . . . When you're comin home, an when she's expectin ye home, if ye do come home," he says, "she's goin tae put him tae lift the flagstone at the fire, and there a trap stair goin down, an," he says, "she's goin tae hide him there in case we come home. But," he says, "when we do go home," he says, "ye'll hae plenty of rabbits an hares probably, see: jist tell her, 'Ye're to pit on the three-fittit pot,' the great big pot, an tell her to boil ye some o the rabbits an hares. Tell her not tae take time to take the guts oot o them or skin them or wash them, jist to pit them in a pot the way they are. Tell 'em it's fir yir three dogs, to boil them up fir yir three dogs, that they're hungry." He says, "Whenever ye get them tae the boil," he says, "take off the pot an leave it be the top o the flagstone. Throw a bit out tae us three dogs," he says. "When ye throw the piece o meat out tae hiz, tae the three dogs, we'll start to fight, an," he says, "Able'll pit his shoulder tae the pot," he says, "an he'll coup it, an," he says, "we'll burn the packman tae death."

"Very good," he says.

So anyway, he's knockin about, oh, but he couldnae carry the rabbits or hares he was gettin: he was gettin them in dizens—every two or three minutes he was gettin big hares, mountain hares and rabbits an everything. He had a bag full. So when he come in, he says, "Oh," he says, "we're aafa hungry. We're aafa hungry," he says. "Gie me the big pot ben tae get some ae the rabbits on tae ma dogs. They're hungry too." So he went ben an he gets the big pot and he pits half a dizen o rabbits or thereaboot in, pits it on the swey, pits it on the fire, boils them up. "Oh, that'll do," he says. "Take them down." Pits them on top o the flagstone, throws a wee bit to the dogs, so the three dogs starts a fight. Able pit his shoulder tae the pot—it was a like a big cauldron, ye know, great big thing—he pits his shoulder tae the pot on this aald broken flagstone—bits out o it—this boilin stuff went down on the tap o this old packman and he's burned to death.

Oh, she's lamentin aboot the house, but she couldnae say nothing, ye see? But hooever, him an the three dogs is away again, and . . . now she has her baby—the packman was the father of it—she has this wee laddie, he's jist aboot a bairn aboot twa 'r three year aald, and he's knockin about the garden. . . . She gets the packman out, and she buries him in the garden, ye see? But this wee boy, he's diggin away at the garden an he comes in wi a sprinter o bone, an she says, "Where did ye get that, sonny?"

"Oh," he says, "A got it out in the corner o the garden thonder, mam." Well ye see, it was a . . . sprinter o the bone jist two or three year maybe after that, that this packman was buriet.

'Oh," she says, "son," she says, "that's surely a bit of yir father's bone. But," she says, "A'll pit it in . . . in yir uncle's bed the night," she says. "When he comes home," she says, "he's a habit of throwin hissel in the bed, an," she says, "A'll pit it up through he's body the night. A'll pay him back." Sae she goes wi this sharp-pointed bone an she places it stickin up like a needle in the bed.

Knowall says tae Jaik. "Jaik!"

"Well," he says, "what's . . . what's this now, Knowall?"

He says, "Their wee boy," he says, "was out in the garden today an fun' a bone. Found a bone," he says, "an yir sister's goin tae be revenged tae you. She's pitten it in yir bed. And fir the—Be careful," he says. "Fir the livin light don't throw yoursel in the bed," he says, "when you go home!"

"Oh, but," he says, "A'll mind that." So home he comes—oh, he couldnae carry aa the rabbits an hares he wis gettin. Anyway, he forgot. He throwed he's sel down backwards in the bed, tae have a rest. Goes right up through he's—inside his heart, right up through him. Then he was dead.

She trails him away down tae a dyke side where there a kind o a moss place, an saft moss, and she jist liftit a wee bit o the sand up ower the mossy, watery ground, an jist throwed him in there and left him lyin. She chased the three dogs away after him.

So the three dogs is sittin murnin on the top o the grave. And Knowall looks, an he sees a . . . a rat and a wheasel fightin. The wheasel killed the rat. Then the wheasel went aff an it brung a wee voyal, a wee bottle, an it took oot the cork, an it rubbed aa the rat ower wi its fingers—or its paws—wi this stuff was in the bottle, an the rat jumpit up livin again.

So Knowall lookit round an he says, "D'ye see that, Able?"

"Yes," he says.

"Did you see it . . . Swift?"

"Aye, yes," says Swift, "I seen it."

"Well," he says, "Able, you knock the dyke down," he says, "I know where the bottle's lyin," says Knowall. "An if it goes tae run," he says, "Swift can catch it."

"Very good." . . . Able pit his shoulder to the dyke an he jist pit the dyke all away, and . . . the wheasel run out wi the bottle in its mouth. So Swift jist catched it the first jump, jist catched the wheasel, took the bottle out of its mouth, digs up the grave, and rubs Jaik all over wi't.

He rubs his eyes. "My goodness," he says, "I've had a long sleep!"

"Aye, yes," says Able, he says, "this is two or three days you've been sleepin," he says, "two days anyway," he says, "you've been sleepin. An," he says, "ye remember on the hill when I told ye," he says, "about yir sister pittin the bone in the bed?"

"Yes," he says, "I do." So he says, "Oh well," he says, "we'll have tae go," he says, "an no go back near about her: we'll go an push wir own fortune."

So they're away. Oh, travellin aw night, up in the night day efter day. He wis a good-lookin young fellow this, jist a handsome young man. But hooever, they travell't on tae they come tae two or three big houses, an Jaik got a job in some big mansion. He got a job. But here, this girl o the big house, she fell in love wi Jack, ye see? So anyway, when he fell in love, he's never—he's mair interestit in the girl he's goin wi now, an he's clean forgettin about his dogs, doesnae mind them, aw here an there an aa shootin, an then away fishin, an—och, his dogs is forgotten.

"Well," says Knowall, he says, "I think," he says, "by the look o things we're not wantit now," he says, "Able." He says, "A think we'll go an push wir own fortune."

But they were away two or three days, three days or four days: all of a sudden Jaik wan night remember't on his dogs. "Oh, by the way," he says, "A haven't seen my dogs this day or two. Where did they go?"

"Oh," says the girl, "I haven't seen them either."

"Well," he says, "I must go an look fir ma dogs."

He's away, but he could get no hilt nor hair o them. No—but he says, "A'm goin to keep this road anyway to see if I can find them." On he goes an he comes tae a wee house at the road side, an he knocks at the door.

"Here," he says, "my good old man, did ye see or hear anything of three dogs?" he says.

"Ah, yes," said the old man. "I tried tae entize them," he says, "over tae me to gie them a bite, but they wouldn't come near me." He says, "They're goin, they seem to be very weary, sore," he says, "their feet an—wis very sore, and," he says, "the were wan a bit behind the other," he says, "it seemed very forlorn't an tired, an," he says, "it . . . went down to that little rush bush over there," he says, "an it vomited up its heart's blood."

"Oh dear me," says Jack, "that's terrible." Down he goes to . . . the rush bush: he spreads his hankiechief out, an he liftit up the dog's heart's blood. Puts it in his pocket; gaes on again. "I don't know," he says, "this is the way they went," he says, "but where A'll find them Dear knows."

Oh, he's travellin on for a long long way, nights an nights, tae he come tae another shepherd's house. He says, "Here, my old lady," he says, "did ye see three dogs, or did ye hear any barkin or anything, any signs o any likenesses of dogs?"

"Ha, yes," she says, "lad," she says, "the other evening the were three dogs passed here," she says, "but A don't think," she says, "they'll be able to bark, for they're very tired an forlorn't lookin. An," she says, "there wan a good bit behint the other like he could hardly walk, an it went down," she says, "tae the little fern down there," she says, "an vomited up its heart's blood."

"Oh dear me," he says, "that's terrible. Thank ye, ma old lady." Sae he spreads his hankiechief out, he lifts the dog's heart's blood an he puts it tae his pocket.

37

Well, he's goin on again tae he comes tae another kind of a cottage, an he calls in there. He says, "Did any o the children," he says, "or any one," he says, "see three dogs passin this way?"

"Yes," says a lump o a boy, he says, "I did see three dogs," he says. "But," he says, "they were very very done-lookin, tired," he says, "sick-lookin, very sore-lookin, could hardly walk." He says, "Wan o them was behint the other," he says, "an it went down over there," he says, "at the bank, tae a heap o grass, an it vomited," he says.

"Oh, thank ye, son," he says, "that's very kind tae tell me." So he goes down an he lifts the last dog's heart's blood and put it in his hankie.

So anyway he walkit on an walkit on tae he comes tae a kind of a big cottage, an he asks there.

"Oh," he says, "there's an old lady here," he says: "they call her," he says, "the Witch of Endor. A wild-lookin old wumman," he says. "An they follaed her. She bides—she stays in a cave," he says, "away at the roughest part o the sea, above the sea. That's where she stays, an," he says, "A seen the dogs follaein her. So you'll have tae go there tae get your three dogs."

So this boy walkit on tae he come tae the cave, an when he lookit in, he says, "Good mornin, ma old wumman," an she lookit around.

She says, "The Devil take away yir learnin, my boy," she says. "It's a good job," she says, "you got the first word of me." She says, "If I'd 'a' haen the first word," she says, "you'd have been torn to pieces."

"Where," he says, "is my three dogs?"

So they were lyin in the corner. "Here we are, master, but we can't come: we've no heart's blood."

He says, "There's yir heart's blood: every wan'll know their own." Sae he took out his hankiechief and spread it on the floor an each wan liftit their own heart's blood.

"Now," says this lady, she says, "that's wir enchantment broken," she says.

When he lookit round there was three young boys, beautiful young men: the three dogs is three lovely young men. He says, "That's my three brothers an this is my foster-mother"—that's the old witch, an she was changed in a witch, you see? So that's the finish o my old story.

The Parson's Sheep

Gib Voy

Away back in the old days in Orkney there were some gey pitiful times. Jimmock o Tissiebist, wi a scrythe o peerie bairns, were warse off than maist: wi the sheep aa deein, and the tatties a failure, things at Tissiebist wisna lookin ower bright for Christmas. Whatever weys or no, one blashie dark night, Jimmock was away a while, and twa-three days efter, an uncan yowe was seen aboot the hoose. Some o the bairns surely kent the yowe, for one day when ane of them was oot herdin the kye, he was singin to himsel aboot it, something like this:

> Me father's stol'n the parson's sheep
> An we'll hae mutton an puddins tae eat
> An a mirry Christmas we will keep,
> But we'll say naethin aboot it.

> For if the parson gets tae know,
> It's ower the seas we'll have tae go,
> And there we'll suffer grief an woe
> Because we stole fae the parson.

Well, up jumps the parson fae the other side o a faelie dyke, and he says tae the boy: "Boy, look here, if you'll come to the church on the Sabbath and sing that same song, I'll gie thee a suit o claes and half a croon."

So, on the Sunday mornin service, efter the minister had read a psalm and said a prayer, he stood up and he said in an aaful lood voice: "I hev the following intimation to make. Stand up, boy, and sing that same song as I heard you singin, herdin the kye."

But the peerie boy hed mair wit than that. This is what he sang:

The Green Man of Knowledge

As I was walkin oot one day
I spied the parson very gay:
He was tossin Molly in the hay—
He turned her upside down, sir.

A suit o claes and half a croon
Was given tae me be Parson Broon
Tae tell the neighbours all aroon'
What he hed done tae Molly!

The Cat and the Hard Cheese

Betsy Whyte

Well, this was an aald woman, you see, an she had two sons, and—nae money as usual, things were hard up, an one o her sons, he wid try an find work an dae this an that, but the ither one, they cried him Silly Jeck; he used tae jist lie—like me—in front o the fire aa the time, an half covered wi ashes an stoor, an he wouldnae bother tae dae anything, an they never bothered him very much tae dae anything, because they jist cried him Silly Jeck. But anyway, everything wis jist comin tae a head an they were gaunna be put oot o the hoose if they couldnae find the rates, an nae money, nae nothin. (The man lang dead, ye see.) So this other brother, John, he says, "Ma, A'll have tae go an push ma fortune," he says, "an see if I can find anything tae keep the roof ower yir heid." So he's away, hi tae the road an ho tae the road an on an on an on an on an on an on—but before he left the hoose his mother says, "Well, ye'd better take somethin wi ye!" She says, "A'll mak ye a wee bannick an A'll fry ye a wee callop," she says. She says, "D'ye want the wee yin wi the blessin, or the big yin wi the curse?"

He says, "Oh, A'll need plenty, ye'd better gie me the big yin." So she fried this callop tae him an she made a bonnick—ye ken, that's a big oatcake—and she put it intae a hankie an away he goes. An he wis gettin weary fae walkin on an on an on an on an on an now he says, "Och, A'll sit doon here"—it wis the side o a wee stream, ye see?—"an A'll get a drink an eat ma bannock." An he's sittin there, an he's sittin eatin an this aal man come alang.

An this small man says, he says, "That looks aafae good, that bannock an that collop."

"Ah weel," he says, "it may look good," he says, "but I need it masel," he says, "fir it's aa A've got, an God knows when A'll get the next."

An the aal man says, "Oh, it's aa rycht, laddie," he says, "I suppose ye're richt enough," he says, "ye're young an ye need yir bite."

So away he went then, on again an on an on again, kept walkin an

walkin an walkin: nae razor wi him or nothin, ye ken, an his baerd wis growin an his shoes were gettin holes in them—no, no: jist hid tae keep goin. But eventually he come tae this gates o a big estate and on the gates it says they were men wanted, ye see? So he went in an he went up an this wis a great big castel he come tae. And he rang the bell at the back door; he says, "A see they're advertisin here fir men."

He says, "Oh aye," he says, "but," he says, "I don't think ye'll ever dae the work."

"Well," he says, "there nae hairm in tryin."

He says, "No, there nae hairm in tryin," he says, "but if ye fail," he says, "ye see aa thae heids stickin on the gate doon there?" he says: "yours'll be the next."

"Ah well," he says, "A cannae help it," he says, "I'd be as weel deid onyway as goin on like this." So they took him in tae the kitchen anyway an they fed him well an gave him a bed and says, "You'll be aa right." An the next night he says, "Ye've tae start yir duties."

So he wis brought before the king an the king says, "Well," he says, "it's three tasks ye have tae do." He says, "If you can do this three tasks," he says, "as naebody his done yet," he says, "ye'll no only get money," he says, "but ye'll get the princess to marry, and," he says, "a place o yir own, and this kingdom when I die."

So he says, "Well, what have A got tae do?"

"Well," he says, "do you see that big bog down there?" He says, "I want that oot o there before mornin." He says, "That's whit ye have tae dae, ye've tae clear it aa before mornin." He says, "There ye go," so he gien him a mutchkin o whisky, and he gave him sandwiches an meat awaa wi him and he says, "Awaa ye go."

So away he went doon, an he says, "There's a baler an a shuffel an everything tae ye." So he goes doon an he starts balin this water, an balin an balin an balin. But it was just rinnin back in as fast as he could bale 't oot. "Oh no, no," he says, "nae use. Na," he says, "I ken what A'm gaunnae do," he says, "A'm clearin oot." So he tried tae run away, but the king's men got him an brought him back, an he's head was stuck on the gates.

So this aald woman's aye waitin for any news o this laddie, ye see, an she waited an waited an waited an waited, but na, na. And, "Oh," she

43

says, "I doot, laddie," she says, "there something's happened tae John," she says; "he's no comin back." She says, "You'll hae tae try an dae something, Jeck," she says, "would ye rise oot o there," she says, "an try an dae somethin?"

He says, "What am A gaunnae dae?"

She says, "I don' know, but ye could go an look fir yir brother, at least," she says. "A'm no able to traivel or nothin."

"Aa richt," he says. So he got up an he gien he's sel a shake, an there was mair—as much stoor aff him as would ha' blin't ye, an ashes an things. But anyway he got up, an he says, "Well, A'll go, Ma," he says, "an A'll see if I can find him an see if I can find any money or anything tae keep the roof abeen yir heid." He says, "Mak me a wee bannick an fry me a wee callop," he says, "afore I go tae tak the road."

She says. "Dae ye want the big yin wi the curse or the wee yin wi the blessin?"

He says, "Ach, the wee yin 'll dae fine," he says.

So she baked him this wee bannick an she fried this wee callop tae him, an she tied it up in a hankie, an he's away, an he's hi tae the road and ho tae the road, through sheep's parks an bullocks' parks an all the high an the low mountains o Yarrow; an there was no rest for poor Jeck, till the birds were makin nests in his heid an the stones were makin holes in his feet, . . . no rest fir him. But he came tae a stream—A don't know if it wis the same stream his brither wis at or no, but he thought he would hae a drink an eat his bannick, ye see. An he sat doon, an he's eatin this bannick and takin a drink ae the water, when this same wee aald man comes up tae him. And he's standin lookin at him like that, an he says, "That smells good," he says, "that scallop an that bannick."

He says, "Are ye hungry, aald man?" He says, "Ye're nae to be hungry," he says. "Here, you tak that bit," he says, "or tak the half."

"No, no, Jack," he says, "ye'll need it."

"Ah," he says, "A'm a young man," he says, "different fae you. Come on," he says, "you tak it." An he gave it tae him.

The aald man says, "We'll share it." So they sat an shared it, an they sat an drunk the water, an they sat an newsed fir a while, an Jack says, "A'll have tae go, though," he says. "A'm lookin fir ma brither," he says. "Ma mither's worried aboot him; an A'm lookin for work o ony kind tae."

The Cat and the Hard Cheese

So this auld man pit his hand in his pocket, but . . . an he says, "A've nothin now, Jack," he says, "but there's a wee box"—an it was just a wee tin box like an Oxo box, ye ken?—He says, "If ye tak that," he says, "mycht haud yir tobacca or onything," he says, "pit it in yir pocket."

So he took it an put it in his pocket. An he gets up an he's away on an on an on an on again, till he came tae this place—well, somebody directed him tae it, says, "There's a place on there," he says, "they're advertisin fir men tae work," he says. "If ye go there ye'll maybe get something." Well, he saw this notice on the gate anyway and he went up tae the castel, an they took him in an they fed him well and says, "Ye'll see the king in the mornin and he'll tell ye whit ye have tae dae."

So in the mornin the king saw him, an he says, "Well," he says, "ye've three tasks tae dae," he says. "Naebody's ever been able tae dae them, but if you can dae them," he says, "you'll get my daughter, the princess, fir a wife, and my kingdom when I die."

"Ah," he says, "I can only try."

"Well," he says, "tonight," he says, "ye'll go doon—ye see that bog doon there?" he says. "I want that cleared."

"Ah me," he says, "wha could dae that?"

"Well," he says, "ye wanted a job, and that's the job, an that's what ye have tae dae."

So anyway they gave him a muskin o whisky, an they gave him meat wi him, tied up ye ken, an away he goes too. An he went doon an he says, "Ach," he says, "there's nae sense in tryin tae dae that," he says, "a waste o time. A'm just as weel tae drink ma whisky an lie doon, an," he says, "if he kills me," he says, "it's jist too bad," he says, "A'll jist hae tae dae." So he's sittin an he says, "Ach, A could dae wi a smoke." So he took out his wee cley pipe, an he says, "A wonder would there be ony tobaccae," he says, "intae that wee box?" He opens up the box, an when he opens up this box, here there wis a wee man in the box. An he says, "Wha're you?"

He says, "I am the noble Jack o Clubs, an whit's your will, master?"

He says, "Whit?"

He says, "I'm the noble Jack o Clubs, and whit's yir will?"

"Will?"

He says, "Whit dae ye want?"

"Whit dae A want?" he says, "'tell ye whit A want." He says, "A want that—" he says. "Well, I dinnae want, but the king wants that shifted before mornin," he says. "That's whit's wanted."

"Oh well," he says, "jist you lie doon an drink yir whisky." So he lay doon an drunk his whisky: he couldnae ha' cared less, he'd jist reached that stage. But in the mornin, when he woke up, this bog was gone: it was jist like a green lawn . . . when he looks.

And he gets up, an he gies he's sel a shake, an . . . he's runnin up tae the castel, and he gave this bell a pull—it was one o yon bells that ye pull oot, ye ken?—he pulls it tae it rattled through aa the castel. An they cam oot—"Whit's aa this noise?"

He says, "Well," he says, "A've come back: that's yir job done."

They took him in, an the keeng's come oot, an he came doon, and he looked—"Aye," he says, "Jack," he says, "ye're a clever man," he says, "but . . . no so clever as yir learnin maister, whoever he wis!"

He says, "Naebody!"

"But," he says, "ye're no finished yet, ye've two ither tasks tae dae. So," he says, "come in;" but oh, he was treated tae the best then, ye ken, he wis given aa good meat, everything, as much as he could drink, a lovely bed an everything: he says, "Now you go an hae a sleep; then A'll tell you whit yir next task is." So the next night he says, "Dae ye see that aald ruin o'a castel doon there?" he says: "it's half o it's doon an half o it's up: well," he says, "it's h'unted wi a giant, and," he says, "you've tae go doon there the nicht an kill the giant," he says. "That's yir next task!"

"Oh," he says, "that, A'll shuin dae that." So he's away doon, wi his whisky an that again, an he went in . . . in this great big damp dungeon o a place, ye ken, an aal castel. He's sittin, an he heard the thump, thump, thump, thump, and . . . this aald ruins was jist shakin wi the noise o this giant's feet. An he looks up, an this wis a giant right enough, three heids on him. "Ohhh!" he says. So he oots wi his wee box, pulls it open quick. He says, "Are ye still there?"

He says, "Aye, A'm still here! Whit's yir will, master?"

An the giant's gettin closer, ye see, an he says, "Do ye think ye could dae onything wi him?"

"Ah, dinnae worry aboot that, Jeck," he says. So he grabbed this sword off the castle wall: he says, "Take a had o it now, Jeck."

And Jeck says, "I cannae dae nothin wi a sword!"

He says, "Go an try."

So he gets the sword: but this sword was jist goin itsel, ye see—first one head . . . skidded to the one side o the castel, an anither heid went skiddin, till the three heads were aff the giant, an Jack sut—he fell doon, he didnae sit doon, he fell doon, an he says, "My God!" So he says, "If I go back," he says, "they'll no believe me that I've killed this giant," so he went an he cut the three tongues oot o the giant's heids, because he'd tried tae cairry the heids wi him, but they were too heavy. So he cut the tongues oot an put them intae a bag, and he flew back tae the castel and he near tore the bell oot o the socket this mornin, with ringin it tae let the king see this three tongues!

"Ah ha," the king says, "ye're really a clever man, Jeck," he says, "but I wish I kent your learnin mester." So he says, "Well, my next task," he says, "is a task," he says, "that you'll no dae, Jeck," he says, "that naebody 'll dae."

He says, "Whit is it?"

He says, "It's a very simple one," he says, "but you'll no dae it!"

He says, "Whit is it?"

He says, "I want you to tell me," he says, "how many stars there is in the sky." So he says, "That's all there is tae it, an if you can tell me that, Jack," he says, "my kingdom's yours an my daughter. So," he says, "there's your whisky, ye can sit an coont them!"

So he goes oot, an he's sittin: he says, "Ah . . . are ye still there?"

He says, "Aye, A'm here," the wee man says, "A'm here," he says, "an A'm the noble Jack o Clubs. Noo whit's yir will, master?"

He says, "Could you tell me how many stars there is in the sky—that's what this king wants tae know."

He says, "No, A couldnae tell ye, but jist go in," he says, "an tell him, 'There are three thousand million, seven hundred and one, an,'" he says, "'if ye dinnae believe me, coont them fir yirsel!'" So . . . he says, "Aye," he says, "jist dae that," he says, "an . . . it'll be a lang, lang time before he can mak ye a leear."

So . . . he near took the bell clean oot this next mornin . . . So the king says, "Did ye find oot?"

"Aye," he says, "seven hundred million . . . " an he telt him onywey.

An he says, "Are ye su—"

"Yes, that's the dead number," he says, "an if ye dinnae believe me," he says, "ye jist coont them fir yirsel."

So the king realised, ye see, that he couldnae dae nothin aboot this, an he says, "Well," he says, "Jeck," he says, "you've won," he says. "You have definitely earned," he says, "whit ye're gaen tae get." He says, "Now A won't go back on my word," he says: "there's my daughter the princess. Ye can marry, an," he says, "A'm no deid yet, but I have a castel," he says, "jist doon the wey a bit, an yeze can have that till I dee."

An he went an telt the princess that she hid tae mairry Jeck. She says, "A'm no mairryin that," she says, "not me, wi aa this whiskers an dirt an baerd an the smell aff o'm," she says, "not me, A'm no mairryin that man," she says, "Faither, A jist couldnae dae it!"

He says, "I've gien my word an you'll jist hae tae dae it!" He says, "Now, ye ken that." So she wisnae very pleased aboot this at aa: "Na, na," she says—she wis tryin tae get oot o it . . . but she kent she would have tae dae what her father said.

So the weddin come roond an everything: but in the mean time, ye see, they had taken Jeck an shaved him an cut he's hair an bathed him an cleaned him all up an put a beautiful suit on him. An when she was standin there greetin an thinkin aboot rinnin awa, they come in, and she looked roon like this. She says, "A've never seen that man before," an she's waitin for Jeck comin in!

An her father says, "Well, here's yir husband!" An she couldnae believe her eyes, he wis sich a handsome man efter he wis aa cleaned up an sorted an dressed up.

So they got mairriet, an they went to live in this castel, and they're happy in this castel—he's fine an pleased, but he says, "There's one thing A'll hae tae dae," he says, "A'll hae tae go back tae ma mither: she'll be winderin whit's keepin me."

"Oh," she says, "that's all right," she says, "we'll both go back." (She spoke kinda p'lite, ye see?) So they got their carriage ready an away they go back this road tae whar his mother lived. An she wis there sittin in the hoose, an she heard the horses' feet on the road jist ootside the door, an she went tae the windae an keeked oot. "Oh," she says, "my God, gentry," she says, "A wonder what they can be wantin: they've surely lost their road!" An he cam oot o the carriage an he cam ower tae the door: she says, "He's comin in here onywey!" An she went oot tae the door tae see if she could help them—thought they were lost or something.

And he spoke tae her and he says—she wis bendin an curtseyin an almost grovellin at his feet, ye ken—he says, "Mither, whit's adae wi ye, wumman?"

She looked up an she says—she couldnae believe her eyes, she says, "That's no you, Jeck, is it?"

"Aye, it's me, mither," an he grabbed her in his airms: he says, "Come on, ye're no bidin here nae langer, ye're comin wi me!" So he took his mother back tae the castel an she led the life o a lady from that on until she died. An in the meantime Jack an his wife had hed twa bonnie bairns.

But he was learnin aa the gentry's cairry-on now, he's horses an away huntin an shootin an all this cairry-on. An he was away shootin one day up in the mountain an he came back. Now when he came back there was nothing there but twa 'r three stones—jist . . . waa stanes.

"Oh my God," he says, "what's happened? Nae castel, nae nothin, jist a rubble o stones. Oh my God," he says, "what's happened here?" An he sat doon; he says, "I dinnae ken whit's happened!"

An he's sittin thinkin an thinkin tae hissel, an this wee black cat come, an it wis rubbin itsel up against his legs, an rubbin up against his legs, an rubbin up against his legs, ye see? An he says, "Oh, pussy, pussy," he says, "if only you could speak, ye could tell me!" an he's clappin this wee cat . . .

"Speak?" she says. "I *can* speak!" She says, "Naebody ever asked me tae speak."

"Well," he says, "could you tell me whit happened?"

"Ah, fine that," she says, "I can tell ye whit happened." She says, "Ye forgot aboot the wee Jack o Clubs, didn't ye, intae the box?" She says, "Well," she says, "it wis the cook an the butler." She says, "The butler found yir aald jaiket that ye kept in the closet wi the wee box in it, an opened it, and so that's whit happened, an your wife's gone."

"Have ye any idea whar—"

"No, I couldnae tell ye," she says, "whar they are or whar they went, but that's whit happen't," she says, "he found the box."

49

"Oh well," he says, "A'll jist hae tae get—A'll hae tae find them," he says, "A'll hae tae find ma wife." So. . . . "Will ye come wi me, pussy?"

"Aye," she says, "A'll come wi ye," she says, "if I can be ony help tae ye, but A've nae idea whar they went!" So they're on an on an on an on ower this moors an mountains an everything, ye see, tearin away.

He says, "It's aafae cauld the nycht, hiv ye any idea where we could sleep, an . . . " he says, "A'm stairvin! Have ye nae idea whar we could get onything tae eat?"

"Well," she says, "doon there at that fairm there's a barn," she says, "an there's a great big kebbick o cheese," she says. "It's hard richt enough, but it would be aa richt, we could eat it. A fine big kebbick o cheese," she says, "it would dae me an you's haert good," she says, "an we could go doon there."

An he says, "Oh, come on!"

"But," she says, "it's hauntit!"

"What is it haunted wi?" he says.

She says, "It's haunted wi a huge rat."

"Oh," he says, "surely you, a big cat like you wouldnae be feared o a rat, wid ye?"

She says, "Ah, A dinnae ken," she says, "this is nae ordinary rat."

An he says, "A cannae help it," he says, "I cannae help it, the hunger's gettin the better o me, A'll hae tae gang doon fir a bit o this hard cheese." So they go doon tae this fairm, intae the barn, an there wis some strae, ye ken, in the barn.

An she says, "Noo, we've got this cheese right enough," an it wis aa richt, apart from bein hard, ye ken, so they sat an they gorged theirsel wi this cheese. Then she says, "Now," she says, "you'd better go in among that strae," she says; "cover yirsel up wi the strae an bide richt in the corner, an don't move—don't breathe," she says, "when this thing comes."

So he got in the corner an she scratched the strae up ower him an he happed he's sel up wi the strae. So in the deid saelins o the nycht the rat came. An he's lyin there an he's peepin through, ye see, an he seen this rat comin in right enough, but it wis jist an ordinary-sized rat. An it come in, and the cat got its back up, ye ken, like this, an "Chhh! Pffph!" an the rat's "Tschch!" an the two o them are at each ither. And they're fightin an tearin an fightin an tearin, an this rat, it's gettin bigger an bigger, an the cat, it's gettin bigger an bigger! An the rat gets bigger an the cat's gettin bigger, an the rat's gettin bigger an the cat's gettin bigger, till Jack's cooried in the corner like this, on his knees, right intae the corner wi the strae ower him an he says, "Oh, me, me!"

But she kept her back tae this corner whar Jack wis so that he wouldnae get crushed, ye see, the cat did. An they fought an fought an fought an fought fir aboot three struckin 'oors, an all the time he's gettin bigger an she's gettin bigger till the barn wis almost packed wi them, an it wis takin her aa her time fir tae keep Jeck safe in this corner under the strae.

But this cat, she says, "When ye see that A'm as good as whit you are, will ye no leave me alane?"

An the rat says, "When ye see that A'm good as whit you are, will you no leave *me* alane?" An he says, "Well, will we hae a truce an jist say one's as good's the ither, an we'll jist leave it at that?"

An the cat says, "Aye; but there's something A would like tae ask ye." An he says, "Whit's that?"

She says, "Hev you any hilt or hair o a strange castel aboot this airts?"

"No, no," he says, "no; but," he says, "A tell ye whit A can dae," he says. "I can gie ye the power tae call all the beasts an ask them."

She says, "Well, you gie me that," she says, "an A'll leave ye alane"—because she near had the eyes oot o this—

So he says, "Well leave me alane then, an A'll tell you," he says . . . "A'll . . . put the power on ye, an," he says, "you can call on all the beasts in the land tae see." So—whew—the rat disappears, an this cat she shrunk back tae her normal size, an she says, "Are ye there, Jeck?"

"Aye, A'm here," he says, "A'm here—whit's left of me's here," he says, "A'm near aa shrunk awa wi the fricht o me."

She says, "Come oot, it's aa richt," she says. "A've got something that'll help us."

So the next day she went oot, and she called this words that the rat had given her, an all the animals startit comin. An they came an they came, an every one wis asked the same question, did they hear any hilt or hair o this castel.

"Na." "No." "No." "No, no." Always no, no, no.

"Ah," Jeck says, "it's nae use," he says, "nae use at aa. Well, if she disnae come," he says, "A'm goin tae throw masel in the wa—"

"Ah, shut up," she says, "what are ye gaein tae throw yirsel in the water fir? We'll get her yet."

So at the last he wis jist giein up when here he seen this wee moose comin: it wis aa half-drookit, an it seemed—it was aa thon drookit wey, ye ken, like a half-droon't moose. An here it comes up. An he says, "Ahh," he says, "we neednae ask you."

"Whit is it?" she says.

"Did ye hear any hilt or hair on a strange castel or a strange—"

"A'm jist new awa fae it!" she says.

"Are ye sure?"

"Aye!" she says. "A'm sure. A'm jist newly awa fae it," she says, "across the border there," she says, "and a beautiful young—"

And she says, "Whar—"

"Oh," she says, "she's aa richt, rycht enough, but she'll no hae nothin tae dae wi this cook: he hes her locked up until she will hae something tae dae wi him."

And he says, "Well," he says, "moose, A tell ye whit A want ye tae dae," he says. "You go back across," he says, "an look, an ye'll see an aald jaiket, and there's a wee roostie box in it," he says. "If you could get that box tae me," he says, "A'll gie ye the bonniest wee locket fir yir neck that ever ye seen in yir life."

"Ah, Jeck," she says, "you're good at promisin, but A bet ye ye're no sae good at giein."

He says, "As sure as God," he says, "if you go back there," he says, "you'll get it."

"But," she says, "hoo am I gaan tae get back across that water?" (This wis a big moat, ye see, ootside the waa.)

The cat says, "Wait, I ken whar tae get across the water. Come doon here." So they come doon tae the water's edge, and she says, "Jack, you lift that stone." So Jack took this great big stone an he lifted it, an this wis a great big toad under the stone. . . . It was either a puddick or a toad, but A think it wis a puddick.

And he says, "Wghgh, whit are ye disturbin folk like this fir, in the middle o the night? Whit are ye disturbin me fir?"

He says, "A want ye tae dae somethin fir me."

"God, God," he says, "could ye no leave folk at peace nae time? whit dae ye want?"

He says, "A want ye tae take this young woman across the water."

"Whit wumman?"

He says, "This wee moose here," he says, "an if you dae that," he says, "ye're all right fir the rest of yir life," he says, "ye'll get everything ye want."

"Ah," he says, "ye're good at promisin, but ye're no sae good at—"

He says, "Honest tae God," he says, "as sure as God, you dae this fir me—"

So this puddick he says, "Get on ma back, then, moose." So the moose got on the puddick's back, an across the water, intae the castel, an up tae whar this aald jeckit wis hingin, ye see? And she dis get this wee box, but she couldnae get it oot. So she gnawed a hole in the bottom o that until it fell doon on the floor, an she pu'd an pu'd an pu'd it till she got it oot. . . . An the puddick says, "Hoo am I gaun tae get this across the water?" An he says, "Aa richt." So he lay on his back, an he says, "Noo, you sit on ma belly—pit the box on there an you sit on the tap o it an had it on my belly, an A'll go backie-weys across the water." And he went across the water like this tae whar Jack wis, an gave—

"Oh," Jack says, to the wee man, "are ye there?"

"Aye, A'm here."

He says, "Is ma wi—"

"Aye, she's all right," he says.

"Well," he says, "A wish she wis back. An," he says, "A wish the cook and this butler, the two o them," he says, "tae be tarred an feathered an pit a match tae." And nae suiner said than the deed wis done, and they were burnt in izel and he wis back wi his wife in his ain castel an everything, and that's the end of ma story. And the last time A wis there,

> A got brogues o butter an clippins o gless,
> An A come slidin doon the brae on ma —. . . .

53

Cheeseparer and Teastrainer

Ethel Findlater, James Henderson

There's a fine story aboot a man that was lookin for a wife wance, and he watched how she ate cheese. So win woman cut a great chunk of this skin and throwed it away: so he thought she was too extravagant, he wouldn't have anything to do with her. And then the second one ate it all: so he thought there was something wrong with her, she was too mean, she ate the skin and all. So the third one gave the skin a bit scrape, you see, and then she ate it: and he married her. Shö was the most successful wife, he thought.

* * *

This fellow from South Ronaldsay, he went off sailing, at sea, and he had gone a trip on a clipper ship; and his mother, she I suppose had heard of tea, but she'd never seen it or knew much about it. So he brought a packet of tea home with him, and Saturday he told her he was going over to the Hope, and he says, "There you are"—he presented her with the tea—"Have a dish of that ready for me when I come home," he says. "I'll be home about six o'clock, and we'll have some tea."

So when he cam home he says, "Well, mother, did you make the tea?"

"Oh, aye, did I."

"Well," he says, "set it down and we'll have it."

"Huh!" she says. "Faith, thu can have it to theesel. I'm no touchin it. Seec stuff I never saa in me life. I pat seeven watters on it afore I got it clean an fit tae eat!"

Jack and the Devil's Purse

Duncan Williamson

Jeck an his auld mither, they steyed on this wee croft, ye see! . . . An och, times wis very hard. . . . His faither deit when he wis aafa young, an he steyed wi his auld mither, an very little to dae—a young man, money wis scarce, things wis bad, an whit could he dae? Nothing. He never got to nae dances, never got to nae parties, he got nothing, he jist steyed with his auld mither—he could hardly buy a stitch o claes tae his sel or nothing. See? . . . He never had a penny to cry his ain. . . . He could ha' coaxed her maybe fir a shillin at a weekend: he wis lucky if he got a shillin in a month, 'cause the auld sowl hadnae one to gie him.

Him and his mither fell oot and they were arguin, ye see. . . . She says, "Laddie, are ye no gaun tae find a job fir yirsel?"

"Mither," he says, "I cannae get nothin to dae," he says, "God bless ma sowl"—an he wis dry, an he hadnae got a smoke, he hadnae got nothin. He said, "If I had two or three shillins," he said, "God bless us," he said, "I'd sell ma soul to the Devil," he said, "fir a shillin a day."

Nae sooner said than done. He came round this corner; here was this gentleman standin at the roadside, an the gentleman spoke tae him—crackit tae him, ye see? He said, "A heard," he said, "whit ye said, Jeck," he said. He said, "Would ye sell yir so——"

"Aye," he said . . . "haert, soul and body," he says, "to the Devil," he says, "for one shillin a day."

"Well, I'll tell ye better'n that, Jeck," he said. He said, "A'll gie ye a purse, an," he said, "in the purse is a shillin, an," he said, "it disnae maitter how often you spend that shillin," he said; "it'll always be there," he said. "But," he said, "you said yirsel 'at ye'd sell yir soul to the Devil, an ye cannae go back on yir word, an," he says, "you tak this purse an enjoy it," he said, "fir a year an a day. But," he said, "in a year an a day," he said, "A'm comin fir you." See?

"Heh-heh!" Jeck said. "Ye come fir me in a year an a day," he said. "If

A've a shilling fir every day in the week," he said, "A'm no carin whether ye come for me in a year an a day or no!"

He gien Jeck—ye've heard of whit they call a saddler's purse: it wis a wee purse that ye jist shoved the tongue through a flap—he gien Jeck the saddler's purse, an he disappear't. Jeck opened the purse: when he looked into the purse, there was a shillin, silver shillin in the purse. "Ah," he said, "that man's makkin a fool o me," he said. . . . "A'm gaun doon. . . . " Doon he goes to the pub, into the first inn: he buys his self a drink, see? He gies the man the shillin; the man flings it in the till an gies him the change back; Jeck put the change in his poaket—he's dyin tae get a keek into the purse, ye see? He keeks into the purse. There wis the shillin back in the purse again! It disnae maitter how often Jeck spent that shillin, it was always back in the purse.

Noo time passed by, an he kept pittin shillins oot an shillins in, an, och, he . . . he wis a rich man, ye ken? 'Cause the mair he took oot the mair he (? wales)—the shillin wis there, see, he could buy anything he wanted. But his mother, she got kin o dubious: she says, "Laddie, whar ye gettin aa this money?"

So, . . . one night he was gettin away well on, ye see, and he turned roond an he telt his mither. He says, "Mither," he says, "A've got a purse."

She says, "You've got it fae the Devil."

He says, "A'm no carin if A got it fae the Devil or no."

She says, "Ye'll ken that when he comes fir ye," she says, "in a year and a day." She says, "Hoo lang hae ye got that purse noo?"

He says, "A've got it fir six month."

"Hah well," she says, "ye havenae lang tae go now," she said. . . .

He said, "Mither, is that true?"

"Aye," she said, "it's true enough." Noo he begins tae get worried, ye see. She says, "There's only one thing for it, Jeck," she says, "ye'll ha——"

He says, "A cannae get redd o it," he says. "There nae wey," he says. "A read it," he says: "if A flung it awa," he said, the next mornin it'd be back in his pocket again, wi the shillin in it, see?

"A'll tell ye," she said: "go doon tae yir auntie," she said . . . "the auld henwife, an tell her," she said, "the story." She says, "Laddie, . . . 'at's definitely the Devil's work," she says, "ye worked wi the Devil."

But he begins to get worried aboot this now, an doon he goes, an he tells the old henwife the story, see, aboot him gettin the purse. "Oh," she says, "Jeck," she said, "there's . . . nae escape fir ye," she said . . . "definitely," she said. "But," she says, "ye'll have tae get redd o it."

"But," he says, "what wey can I get redd o it?" He said, "I tried to fling't awa, an," he says, "it come back. An," he says, "every time A fling't awa," he said, "A cannae burn it, A cannae do nothin wi 't, an," he says, "it ends up in ma poaket every time, an," he said, "it's definitely the Devil's work." See? Noo he begins to get feart.

She says, "A'll tell ye," she says: "ye'll go up," she says, "to the blacksmith . . . tae the smiddy. An," she says, "ye'll tell him the story 'at ye telt me. And," she said, "mak him," she says, "put it on the anvil, an get a horse's shoe, an heat it . . . tell the blacksmith to heat the horse's shoe in the fire, tae it gets red hot—white hot—an lay the purse on the anvil an tell him to walt it as hard as he kin on the tap of the purse on the anvil."

Jeck says, "What guid'll that dae?"

"Oh well," she said, "you go ahead an dae what A'm tellin ye," the auld henwife said.

Away Jeck goes, up tae the blacksmith, tells the black———

"Oh aye, laddie," he said, "definitely," he said, "it's the Devil's work," he said, "but," he says, . . . "A'll get the Devil in a minute." The auld man got a big Clydesdale shoe and he got a pair o tongs, an he pit the Clydesdale shoe into the fire. "Noo," he says, "Jeck, watch this. Watch tae ye see what ye're cairryin in yir poaket." . . . He pit it on the tap o the anvil, the wee leather purse, an he took a hot shoe oot, an he startit waltin. An he walted it, an every time he hit it, a imp—ye ken the Devil's imps?—a imp jumped oot, an off through the door. An the more he waltit, the more imps come oot, tae he walted it and he walted it and he near walted it in shreds: an the last time he waltit, out jumps the Devil, the real man 'at gien Jeck the purse.

"Noo," he says, "A told ye, Jeck," he said, "that A wis comin back fir ye," he said. "Do you think," he said, "because you waltit all my imps," he said, "oot o my purse," he said. . . . "Ye cannae destroy me." He said, "You're comin wi me," he said, "A come fir you."

"Well," Jeck says, "there's only one thing fir it," he says, "A'll have tae go. But," he says, "look," he said, "A'm gaun away," he says, "to Hell." He says, "A ken it's Hell A'm gaun tae. But," he says, "A'm no deid." He says, "What're ye gaein to dae wi a livin body in Hell?"

An he says, "A've got a job for you, Jeck," he said, "in Hell. You're comin wi me to Hell," he said. . . . "A'm takin ye to Hell."

"Well," Jeck says, . . . "A'll go wi ye to Hell now, but," he says, "look, when you get me tae Hell," he says, "mind," he says, "A'm no deid! An," he says, "as far as A'm concern't," he says, "you're no ma maister. A'm goin wi ye willinly," he said, "because A made the promise to ye, but," he says, "when A get there," he says, "dinnae think," he said, "ye're gaen tae command me like ye command aa the rest o the folk 'at dees, because A'm no deid." See?

"Good enough," says the Devil. "You come wi me." . . .

But Jeck says, "Wait a minute," he says, "A've one thing tae tak before A go."

"What is it?"

He says, "A want to go to ma mither's hoose." (See? Noo, A forgot tae tell ye this bit: the owl' woman telt him, she says, "Look, Jeck, if he ever comes fir ye," she said, "remember," she says, "tae keep the Bible in yir poaket." See?)

The Devil says, "Right," he says, "but," he says, . . . "A'm no lettin ye oot o ma sight."

"Oh," Jeck says, "A'm no wantin ye oot o ma sight," he said. "Ye can come wi me if ye want." Jeck walks into the hoose, taks the Bible, pits it in his poaket: "Now," he says, "come on."

Away him an the Devil goes. An they waak, ken, and they waak on an on, down this road an through this clifts an rocks, an aa the places that the Devil tuk him. But anyway they landit in Hell. . . . An Jeck says, "Noo ye've got me here," he says, "what ye gaen to do wi me?" He says, "A'm no deid," he said, "A'm a human bein," he says.

"A ken," says the Devil, "but," he says, "A've a job fir ye," he said. . . . He says, "Luk ower in that corner," he says, "the back o that gate ower there," he says, "steel gate"—an there they're sittin. Imps o the Devil, aa the imps ye ever seen. "Noo," he says, "that's your job," he says, . . . "A want you," he says, "to look efter them," he says, "take care o them. . . . A'm gaun awa," he said, "fir a lang holiday, an it's your job," he said.

Jack and the Devil's Purse

Jeck says, "No," he said. "Luk," he said, "A'm no takin care o them," he said.

The Devil says, "Luk," he said, "there's sticks there," he said, "an coal, an peats, an," he says, "mak yir ain fire, but," he says, "ye dinnae need to stan at ma fire," he says, "because," he said, "ye're no deid yet. But," he says, "make yir ain fire ower there," he says, "an you look efter these imps," he says, "tae A come back."

"Well," Jeck says, "A'll luk efter 'em," he said, "tae ye," he said: "A promised," he said, "but," he said—Noo the Devil's promise wis that Jeck was only supposed to bide a year an a day wi them, wi the Devil an the imps, ye see?—So Jeck says, "A'll take care o yir imps," he says, "A'll watch 'em fir ye," he said. An they're lukkin through at Jeck, through this airn gate, see? Oh, the most dinky little things ye ever seen, Devil's imps . . . wickit. Jeck wisnae carin!

So the Devil went away. Jeck got his ain fire an his ain sticks an he kennelt this big monster fire an he sut doon an took the Bible oot, ye see? An he's readin away in the Bible, ye see. Noo these imps could peek, see? an tae keep his self fae wearyin, Jeck read aloud, oot the Bible, see? Noo these imps always were quate, an they're listenin: they never haerd nane o this before in their life, see? An they come to this airn gate an they're keekin through at Jeck, ye see?—Jeck telt them to behave theirsels, see. But they started speakin tae him an askin what he wis daein. An he quietened them all doon—no-one lookit nor touched him—an he teached them religion. An he was wi them fir a year an a day, an he made them as holy as angels! He made 'em as holy—no more o their wickitness, spittin or arguin or fightin each ither—they were the most holiest imps in the world when Jeck got them fir a year—but, a year an a day, an it wis only minutes he wis supposed to be, ye see?

But the Devil come back, see? An he'd got this old man on his back, ye see, he's draggin this old man back. . . . This wis a deid man he came back wi on his back, ye see? . . . An he poked up his big fire, an he flung the old man on the tap of the fire, an he shouted fir the imps: he says, "Come on," he says, "get workin on the tap ae him," he says, "an get him trementit." See? He open't the gate. Na, the imps wouldnae gae near him. The imps all gaither't roond Jeck. They widnae do nothing fir the Devil, no way, they widnae work fir the Devil no wey.

He says, "Jeck, whit did ye dae wi my imps?"

Jeck says, "They're nae imps nae mair," he said. "They're angels," he says, ... "A converted 'em," he said. "While ye were awa on yir holidays," he said, "A taught them," he says, "oot the Bible," he says, " ... tae be real angels," he said, "holy," he said. "They're no no more imps."

"Well," the Devil said, "luk," he says, "you're no deid," he says, "an A cannae command ye. But," he says, "luk," he says, "A gien ye peats," he says, "an A gien ye matches. An," he said, "ye're too bad fir Heaven, an," he says, "ye're too good fir Hell. An," he says, "A gien ye peats an sticks an ye kennelt a fire tae yirsel, an," he says, "you convertit my imps," he says, "into angels. Now," he says, "you go on your way," he says; "take them with ye."

Jeck says, "Right," he says, "A'll go on ma way," he said, "an," he says, "A'll take them with me." So Jeck tuik 'em all wi him fae Hell.

Noo that's whar goblins ... come fae, ye ken? ... Wee goblins an wee people—Jeck took them wi him to the forest, and he let them go, an he says, "Now go on your way," he said, "an be good," he said, "fir the rest o yir days," he said. "An always be good," he said, "an always dae good turns to people." And that wis the origin o the elfs an goblins ... in this world today. An they're still there. You [can] believe it!

Jack went back tae his mither, an never again did he accept money fae the Devil. An that's the end of ma wee story.

The Devil at the Foul Ford

Jack Cockburn

My grandmother told me that her mother had told her the story about the family of Neill who came down from Aberdeenshire, either because they had taken part in the '45 or they had got into some terrible trouble, but they were very much disliked where they were and they thought it was better to move. They were blacksmiths, so they came down and they took the blacksmith's shop at Longformacus (which is still in evidence, with the horseshoe over the door) and they settled there. But they were pretty wild when they were up north, and they were just as wild when they got to Longformacus, but they settled down and they worked quite hard. And after they'd been there for a time, I think I'm right in saying it was one of the Duchesses of Roxburghe who'd died, and of course they owned Byrecleuch, close into Longformacus—it would be the old Neill's duty to go to her funeral, which was at Kelso.

So he walked to the funeral, and came back with some people he had got to know in Greenlaw, and stayed there and probably had one dram after another, and then he set out for home. And I think it was summer time, because he took a near-cut . . . he cut over from the far end of Greenlaw Moor over between the Dirringtons, as a near-cut for Long-formacus—that's roughly the line, though I haven't been it myself. He didn't get home till about five or six in the morning, when his wife heard a fearful crash at the door, and when she opened it the father was lying semi-conscious: and they carried him in and put him to bed, and he lay in a very dazed condition all day. And then about two o'clock in the afternoon he asked to see the minister, and the minister came in—which was a very unusual thing for any of the Neills, to ask for the minister!—but he told them that he wanted everybody to go out: he wanted to have a private word with the minister. And the minister listened to a long story and came out; and he died that same evening.

And the minister said he'd made him a long statement, but he was to say nothing about it, except for this: that he was to be sure to warn all the members of the Neill family that whatever they did, they must never use the near-cut across from Greenlaw to Longformacus again as long as they lived, because they would rue the day.

So they thought nothing of this. The young man was aged to carry on the blacksmith's shop, and all went well for a good many years, and then there was a Border Union Show or something at Kelso, and the young man set out to go to that again. Again he stayed with somebody in Greenlaw, or certainly was pretty late on the road, and it was a summer night definitely: and young Neill never came home at all. And the next day they went out to seek him, and they found his body in one place, and his waistcoat was hanging on a whin-bush, and he was terribly scratched and bruised, and had been killed by something, and they could never solve . . . the marks—they were like deep claw-marks on his face and all over him, and he was dead.

Well, the minister that was at Longformacus when the father's death and the son's death [happened] then said that he felt that he was at liberty to say what the old man had told him. The old man had told him that he'd set out from Greenlaw, and he'd got down to what is now known as the Foul Ford, and he heard a noise of horsemen coming behind him. And when he looked over his shoulder, here was a funeral coming, with horses and riders, and a hearse and the horses with the black plumes, and up driving the hearse was the Devil. Sitting up in the coffin was the Duchess of Roxburghe—so they say. But he saw it coming and he ran for all he was worth in the sort of . . . half-light, and the Devil whipped up the horses and came after him and . . . eventually they chased him till it was broad daylight, and he escaped them. But the Devil shouted out and he said: "The first time you or one of your family come this way, I will have you."

And that was the reason why the second one met with an extraordinary death. If it had been lightning he'd have been burned; if it had been any usual thing, marks would have shown; but his face and body were so badly torn and scratched and he was lying dead.

The Angel of Death

Stanley Robertson

This story starts aff awaa back over a hundred years ago. Up at Ballater there wis a faimly o traivlers livin, an their name wis MacDonald. The man wis cried Big Davie MacDonald, an he's wife wis cried Maggie. An Davie wis a fine big strappin man, an he wis a perfect tinsmith, he wis able tae work wi silver, wi gold; he could work wi knifes, he wis able tae use aa the kind o tricks o he's trade. He's wife, noo, her job wis jist bein a good hoosewife, to look efter the caravan an see that he's meals an things wis properly in order. They were wealthy traivler folk; they had a lovely caravan, their caravan was beautifully painted up in green and gold. Inside he'd aa kind o bonnie ornaments, gold an silvers, pewter, brass an copper, an folk used tae come fae far an near—the ither traivler folk came from far an near to admire this beautiful caravan. And they caa'd it the Evenin Star, because it used tae shine at nicht under the moon light, wi aa the gold an silver.

Noo this folk hed only but one laddie, an 'is laddie hed maybe been aboot twelve year aald, an he's name wis Johnnie. An although he wis only the one son, he hed tae ken how to look fir his livin. Noo, he could dee a wee bit o the work 'at he's faither did, but he wisnae quite bein trained fir that work; he wis bein trained tae be able to dry-hunt, to be able to hawk fir he's sel, because he meant, sometime he would be on he's own, an he wouldnae be able to . . . depend aye on he's folk. At twelve year aal at that time laddies were looked upon as young men, an they'd to be sort of independent an be able to look fir their ain livin. So Johnnie used to . . . ging wi maybe a basket o stockins, or he would maybe ging roon dry-huntin or get skins or things roon aboot the cottar-hooses up 'e Deeside, roon aboot the Ballater area far aboot they normally bade. (Though sometimes they would' movit, maistly they bade at Ballater.) Johnnie wis a happy, pleasant kind o a laddie, an he wis able

63

to mak his livin, an his folk didnae worry aboot him fan he went awaa oot the road: he used to jist leave in 'e mornin an waak he's two or three miles, an he would dee the wark 'at he wis set oot tae dae.

But ae time at a late summer Johnnie wis aboot nine or ten mile awaa fae Ballater, away up the Deeside, an he wis gettin aafa tired 'at nicht; he hed waakit an aafae distance an he wis feelin very very wearied. An he says tae hissel, "Och, A think A'll gan awaa haem, an A could dee if a horse an cairt would come along, so I can get a lift doon 'is road." An he waaks wearily alang this road, an it wis beginnin tae get gloamin. An as he waaks along this road, he hears the sound o the horses comin along, he hears the hoofs o the horses comin an he can hear a carriage, an he kenn'd be the sound o it 'at this wis gaan tae be a bigger kind o carriage. He says, "Well, A'll try tae get on tae this coach, an A'll wave the rider doon an see if A'll get in."

An sure as Death, alang the road comes a grea' big carriage an six bonnie white horses. An he waves it doon, an sittin up at the drivin part there's a tall lean man. An he says, "Fit dae ye want, laddie?"

An he says, "Well, is there ony chance o me gettin a lift? A'm gaan tae Ballater."

He says, "Well, I am gaan tae Ballater alang the road," he says, "but A'm nae jist gaan directly," he says. "A have one or two collections tae mak, but if ye want tae come up an sit beside me, you can sit here an keep me company, an 'at'll be fine company fir me alang the road"—an he wis an aafa pleasant, cheery man.

Sae up jumps Johnnie ontae the . . . the high coach, an in the back o . . . far he wis sittin there wis a windae, an he could look intae the windae, and he sees a young kin' o woman sittin in 'e coach. An he says, "Och well, this must be takin folk awa tae some kin' of a baal or something 'at's gaan tae be on." So aff the coach goes awaa wi the horses intae the night, an he turns aff intil a lonely road; stops at a hoose. An in jist aboot half a minute oot comes anither woman, a big stoot woman, an she's on a lang funny kin' o flowing, white kin' o goon, an a queer shapit kind o hat on her heid. An she comes oot the hoose, waaks tae the carriage, an very starey an glazy-eyed, comes inside.

An Johnnie says til her, "Good evenin, missiz!"—bein kind o polite an friendly. And she disnae speir a word til him: she gans in an she sits doon. An Johnnie looks at her through the wee gless windae at his back, an she disnae say "Good evenin" tae the ither woman 'at's sittin beside her. An Johnnie thinks til hissel, "'At's queer: 'at's usually fin ye meet somebody in a carriage, ye usually say 'Good evenin' tae them." But awaa the carriage goes again, the coach an horses off intae the night, an 'e driver starts newsin again tae Johnnie, an lauchin an tellin him mair jokes. And then he turns aff anither big lang road, away up by the wuids, an stops at anither hoose.

An oot there come an aald man, an he wis dressed in a queer kind o goon, an a lang kin' o sleeping cap, an he come on tae the carriage. An he disnae say nothing tae her, but he jist comes doon an sits aafa quietly. An 'en awaa the carriage goes again, tae they come til anither hoose, an oot comes a young woman, a very beautiful young woman with her long flowin auburn hair in the night. An her eyes were glazey, an she—a strange sort o aura went aa roon aboot her. An she comes intae the carriage, an sits doon. And still neen o this folk his speired a word tae een anither, an they hannae even bade een anither "Good evenin". Off the carriage goes eence again.

But by noo it wis gettin fairly late on at nicht, an it start to come doon drizzlin rain—nae heavy, but 'on thick kind o rain 'at jist seems tae sink fair in an freeze the marra o the bones, an Johnnie begin tae get aafa chilled and shivery, an he says, "A'm gettin a bittie seek sittin here in 'is cauld." So this man drives up anither road tae he comes til anither hoose, an he says tae Johnnie, "Noo, laddie, A'm five minutes airly at this hoose. Jist you wait here an A'll be back oot, an then A'm gaan tae Ballater."

So fin 'e man gings awaa tae 'is hoose, Johnnie wis sittin under 'is wee snoot o . . . a cap 'at wis ower his heid, and he wis gettin aafae aafae caul an chill. An he says, "Well, the carriage is a grea' big carriage an it's nae full yet," he says. "A'm gan tae sit in here fir a wee whilie." Sae doon he climbs, hings on tae the carriage, an sits doon in one o the empty spaces. An he says, "Good evenin, folks, it's an aafa coorse kin' o nicht it's turnin." An there's nae a soond answer't. An he looks intae their eyes, an they're aa starin fae a glarey eye at een anither. An he feels a strangeness aboot this folk. An he says, "This is the queerest folk A've ever seen," he says. He says, "Maybe 'is is folk gan awaa tae some kin' of a madhoose," he says. "A'm gan tae sit doon aff here," he says, "A'll . . . close the door."

An he rins, an he gings under the eaves o the hoose. An he stands, an he says, "A'll shelter here tae the driver comes oot."

An jist far he wis shelt'rin fae the rain, there wis a windae, and he looks intae the windae; an the Tilley lamp wis on, an he could see fine in the windae. An there wis an aal man lyin on a baed; there wis a meenister, an a stoot woman fa wis roarin an greetin; an as Johnnie comes nearer tae the windae, he hears the minister sayin tae the aul woman, "Well, the auld man has jist passed away." And Johnnie gets a richt fleg, an he thinks til he's sel, "What a time tae look in at a windae, jist when somebody has newly died!" An jist a few seconds efter 'at he notices the driver o the coach come intae the room: an wi a wave of he's hand tae the deid corpse, beckons it to rise. An up the auld man rises oot o he's death bed, an waaks oot the hoose. But as Johnnie sees 'is, he flees right back tae the carriage, climbs up on the driver's part o the coach, an sits under the snoot. He kens fa this is he's sittin wi. He says, "This is the Angel o Death 's here!" An he says, "I mustnae let him ken that I ken fa he is." Then he comes back, pits the aal man intae the coach, an up he comes.

But 'is driver wis sic a pleasant man an sic a friendly man, Johnnie felt at ease wi him. An then the driver says, "Well, that's aa ma collections fae here, ma next collection's in Ballater." An off they gae intae the nicht, an away, fleein like the wind. Finever they see Ballater in sight, finever they were aboot half a mile fae Ballater, Johnnie says, "If ye jist stop here, driver, A'll get aff here, an—I jist bide aboot 'is part." 'Cause he wanted aff the coach noo as quick as he can; he disnae want tae bide in it. So fan he comes doon aff the coach, the driver looks doon intae him an says til him, "Weel, laddie, A'll see you again. It winnae be fir a lang time yet, but you an I will meet again, and you will get to come in this carriage. A'll gie you a hurl again in this carriage thon ither time."

An Johnnie says, "Well, A hope it's nae for an aafa lang time afore I get this hurl!" So jist as the coach is gaen awaa intae the night, Johnnie shouts oot, "Far aboot in Ballater are ye makkin yir collection?"

An jist as the carriage is gan away oot o sight, the man shouts back, "A'm gaan to the caravan site, an A'm gaan tae the Evenin Star!" An a paën fair shoots through Johnnie's haert. The Evenin Star wis his mither and father's caravan.

Sae he rins noo, an he rins aa the wey tae try an beat the coach in, to waarn his folk that the Angel o Death's comin, so he's rinnin aa the wey as fast as he can, but fin he gets tae this part o Ballater, the ither end o Ballater, far he wis bidin, here wis the beautiful Evenin Star in an inferno, jist burnin to the high heavens, an aa the folk roon aboot it in the night.

An Johnnie starts to roar an greet oot o him an scream blue murder: he thinks noo that he's folk's burnt, an that the Angel o Death has came fir them. But as he's greetin an screamin, he's mither comes til him, an he's mither says, "Fit's adae wi ye? Ye're in an aafa state!" An he sees he's father stan'in 'ere, an the man says, "Fit's adae wi ye, laddie?" An he cuddled an he kissed he's parents, he tells he's mither the strange, strange experience o the night that he'd gane through. An fin he'd finished he said til his mither, "Why wis it that the Angel o Death came tae this caravan, an yet he's left empty-handed?"

Then he's mither looked at him jist fir a minute, an she says, "Well, maybe he didnae ging awaa empty-handed."

An Johnnie says, "But . . . youse are here!"

She says, "Aye, me an yir faither wis oot," she says, "but Princie, the dog, wis in the caravan fin the caravan caught fire, sae the Angel o Death didnae ging awaa empty-handed efter aa."

The Bridegroom and the Skull

Tom Tulloch

This young man . . . — he was been doin his coortin, an it was come on to the time 'at he was goin to mairry. An it wis customary here in Shetlan 'at the bridegroom aalways took the best man wi him when he güd to pit in his proclamaesheen. But he hed a braw bit to traivel afore he cam to the best man's hoose. An he hed a peerie lappie o a dog that ay followed him every wey he güd. And the proclamaesheen wis ay pitten in ipö the Setterday night, an the proclamaesheen wis procleemed i the kirk ipö the Sunday. So he set oot fae the hoose this night . . . an the dog wis at his heels, an he güd fir the best män's hoose on his rodd goin to the manse; and they were a kirk yaurd 'at wis closs by whar he hed to go. An efter he wis passed the kirkyaurd, then he noaticed 'at the dog wisna wi him. He turned him back to look fir the dog, an then he fand the dog kind o playin him wi a skull an krawin upon him. An he took the skull fae the dog and he hoidit the skull inunder a brae, an while he wis hoidin the skull inunder a brae he said to the skull, "If thu'd been livin thu could have come to my weddin a week o Wednesday!" But efter he wis pitten by the skull he güd an collected the best män and they güd to the manse and they pat in the proclamaesheen, an . . . the banns were duly procleemed ipö the Sunday, and the weddin took place some time t'rough the week.

An efter the mairriage ceremony wis been preformed, they güd to the bride's hoose to hae the recepsheen—an it wisna in his owen village, this wis a toonship a braw bit awey, an he wis done the moast o his coortin aboot the night, so he wisna jist that awful weel awhantit wi the toonship—but when the weddin recepsheen wis nearly at its height, they were een o the weddin guests 'at came til him an said that they were some body come to the door 'at was waantin to spaek wi him. So he laid aside whatever it wis 'at he was doin an he güd to the door; an this appeared to be a fairly weel-dressed streenger män 'at wis staundin at

68

the door, and the män said 'at he would have likit to ha' spoaken tae him fir a peerie moament. So he steppit ootside, an the män moationed til him 'at he wis to come wi him. And he güd efter the män, and the män güd intil a hoose an the bridegroom güd wi him. An he t'owt 'at he wisna noaticed the hoose afore, but the night wis been spent an he wis a kind o a streenger in yon toonship, an besides that he wis hed two 'r three refreshments an he peyed no graet atteensheen, but he güd in. An when they cam in . . . the streenger man moationed to him to set him doon upon a sairtan chaer. An he set him doon and they stairted to spaek, but the bridegroom different times said 'at he dooted he would hae to go. And the streenger he rase up, and they were a caundle lowin ipö the taeble an he pat a screp ipö the caundle wi the nael o his t'oomb, and he said 'at they would spaek until the caundle burned doon to yon mark. So they sat an spak back an fore, an the bridegroom wis lookin aroond him an he happened to look up i the röf, an warna they a mill ston hangin abün his heid, an the oanly thing 'at wis haddin him up was the hair oot o a human heid! An he got brawly alairmed aboot this, an he prepare't to rise up, but the streenger said til him 'at he needna be faered to sit still, "Fir," he says, "as du widna let thy dog hort me yon night 'at du lighted in wi me i the kirkyard, the millston 'll no hort dee while thu's sittin yondroo. An becaze thu invited me to the weddin A'm come!" An then the bridegroom realised wha it wis 'at he wis spaekin til, an he said ageen 'at he dooted 'at he would hae to go, and they lookit at the caundle, an the caundle was just come til aboot the mark. And the streenger said that was aa right, he could rise an go.

So he rase up an he güd, an be yon time the first creak o day was comin up and he made fir the hoose 'at the bride was atil an the reception was goin aheid. But as he cam up ower fir the hoose he t'owt 'at it wis all very kind o dull an black-like. But he oapen't the door an he güd in, an when he cam in, to his surprise the oanly thing 'at he saw there wis a elderly wife takkin up the aes an goin to kindle up the fier aboot the moarnin. And he lookit aroond him in graet surprise an he said to this wife, whät wis come o the weddin company 'at he left here a peerie while fae syne?

And shö said, weddin company? They were been no weddin company here i hir time!

An he said shö wis shörly doitin, fir it wis no graet lenth o time fae he left a weddin company an his bride here an everything was goin föll swing.

An shö said, Güd be aboot him! Shö said 'at . . . they were been no weddin company here i hir time, but shö said shö believed that shö heard her grauntmither sayin 'at they wir a weddin 'at took place i this hoose, and that 'at the bridegroom güd forth to spaek some body, and he . . . wis never been heard tell o fae syne!

And when he heard yon, then he realised what wis teen place—that he wis been fort' far an far longer as ever he thowt, an he just drappit doon in a haep o stoor ipö the middle o the flöir; and shö sweepit him up wi the bözom and shö took him up wi the aes an pat him fort', an that wis the end o him!

The Three Yells

Charlie Laurenson

This story . . . it was caa'd jist the story o the Three Yells. It was supposed to happen in Dale o Delting, an they were twa hooses there, twa faimlies livin in them. Ecn o this men deed. A while efter, his neebor man, he dreamt t'ree nights runnin 'at this man 'at wis deed was gaun to speak wi him, an he was wantin him to come—that wis ipae the other side o the voe, a place they caa'd the Holl o Cudda: it was famous fir trows. An he wis to come there at midnight an tak the mare wi him, . . . the work-horse 'at he hed. So . . . when he dreamt the t'ree nights runnin he thowt 'at he would hae to . . . do somethin aboot it, so he took the mare an güd an wis there at the appointed time. An this man appeared 'front o'm. He said 'at he couldna bide long, becaze it wis a job to him to get back to this world again; but what he wantit to tell him was 'at his wife was hevvin an affair wi anither man, an . . . since they were ay been good freends an that, he thowt he would lik to come back an pit him wise to this. Then he said he would have to go, but he wis to get on his mare's back an mak for hom as quhick as he could, and he would hear three yells: and if he wisna inside the hoose afore the third yell, he would be a daid man, he would never win hame alive.

Onywey he got on the mare's back an set aff doon the . . . doon alang the rodd. When he cam to the . . . comin to the head o the voe, it wis a ebb, an . . . that shortened his journey a braa bit, becaz there a houb there 'at ebbs an flows, an he could cut right across: they were nae fences there then. When he was comin down to the shore . . . he heard this first yell, just a very moderate yell. This kind o spurred him on a bit, an he made across the voe as quhick as he could, an when he was comin up fae the banks at the ither side he heard this second yell: he was a bit looder. But this made him aa the faer'der—he was beginnin to get a bit worried noo aboot when this third yell would come: he tried an encouraged the auld mare as much as he could to go up—it's braaly steep

72

up to the hooses there. . . . The door o the hoose wis oapen, the light wis shinin oot, an this wis somethin to him to mak for. An just as—be the time 'at he wis gotten there, he wis that excited an he just rade the mare straight in the door o the hoose. Just as she güd in the door, this third aaful lood yell wis heard: an the man wis safe, he was in under the lintel o the door, he was in by the lintel; but the mare—the back end o the mare wis still stickin oot the door, an she drappit daid oot under him.

The Death of James Smith

Jamesie Laurenson

Well, this stoary concerns a män who . . . was supposed to come from Orkney, Deerness in Orkney, and this män was sent to . . . take up fish-curing for Sir John Mitchell. He's generally spoken of as James Smith of Smithfield, but actually this shouldn't be—it was his sons that built Smithfield, or really Gilbert Smith who built Smithfield in 1815. James Smith, actually, they built the Böth of Funzie for him. An he started fish-curin. But seein that they were money in this fish-curing go he decided to braek with his employer an go out on his own, which he did when he had made enough o cash. An so he, like aal the rest o the proprietors then, supplied boats to Fetlar, . . . and the lines; but that was a crushing burden to the fishermen because what they waanted . . . the shares that they waanted for the fish would kept the fishermen poor—just like . . . slaves, you might say. But that's not the stoary.

James Smith thrived till he became a rich män, wän way or another: he purchased a lot o länd, and so he became . . . a noatable män, you may say. 'Course the time came 'at James had to lay him down on his bed an leave it aff, an that so happened to him. And being a noatable män—it was the custom in those days 'at they waeked the dead, but where you got the noatable män dying there were two . . . they were generally ministers 'at was fir that duty. The two men who undertook that, him bein a member o thir church, the Established Church, was James Goardon and James Ingram. And they stopped i the house when the boady was lyin there, till it was böried—the funeral. An bein a noatable män, it was suggested a sixtareen go to Lerwick for a oak coffin, which was done.

And this two ministers was sitting—the boady was in the North Room o the Haa o Funzie (incidentally that house is still up now, believe it or not, and the room 'at that happened is still there), and they were setting in the South Room wi their two-candle chandelier lookin at a rare old expensive family Bible, the two o them, maybe coming on til about, say—well comin on to maybe midnight there, when they heard a noise like knocks . . . a noise in the room. And the wän minister looked to the other. James Goardon said to the younger män, to James Ingram, he said, "Go an see what's to do there in the room."

And Ingram said, "I couldn't go."

And says Goardon, "Are you frightened?"

He says, "Yes, I—frankly I am frightened to go."

"Well," says James Goardon, "but A would go in the room if the Devil was in the room." An he quickly rose up an took the . . . chandelier with him in his hand an went an oapened the room. When they came there the corpse o James Smith was sittin up, an the chinstrap that tied around the face was undone; he was sitting up, looking at them. And Goardon says, "What is to do with you?"

"Well," he says, "I can't get rest to me soal where I've been. . . . I have to come back to reveal things that's troubling me, 'at I didn't ask a repentance before I died."

Says Goardon, "Well, you're waited a long . . . time. Could you not ask before you died?"

He says, well, no, he didn't. But he says, "Could God forgive me at this late hour, now?"

"Well," he says, "you could ha' asked sooner, but all things is possible with God. But what's troubling you?"

"Well," he says, "I've some things to reveal that I did—I know that I sinned. I put Osie Taet off his länd an took his croft;" (incidentally Osie Tait was Reid Tait of Lerwick, the famous Lerwick merchant's grand-father) "I cheated a män out of thirteen shillins 'at couldn't count English coin, off a fat cow 'at I bought to him. (Second.) Thirdly, I gev away Marion Jamieson's two sons, I gev their name o where they lived and the Press Gang captured them an put them in the Towböth o Funzie and they were taken away fae this widow. . . . That's whät A'm repenting now. . . . An you say that God could forgive me?"

"Yes, well, aal things are possible with God, but you could ha' axed sooner."

"Well," he says, "on that assurance I lay me down agaen in peace."

But . . . not long after—that story went through Fetlar and some folk thought it a very strange story, but bein told by this two graet truthful ministers they couldn't say 'at it was wrong, so they accepted it, more or less. But i those days the meetins o the Presbytery an aal that was held i Tingwall. And they went—it mustered there about important Church business. And Goardon arrived there first, and they didna start the meetin, but aal this was so fresh in his mind, he was so much amazed by this experience that he told them. And the oald Moderator, oald Leather-head, a Scotchman, said, "We are not going to say or debate whether the days of meracles are past: that we don't know. But I can hardly get my mind around to believe what you are saying."

Says Goardon to the man, "Well, are you inferring that I am telling a lie?"

He says, "No, no, I am not saying that, but this must be some . . . optical or some illusion in your mind, or you're thinking it happened, it really didn't."

He says, "Well, the member for Unst will be due here in the afternoon, James Ingram, and you can check up my stoary with—ask him." And in due course Ingram arrived.

The old Moderator said, "Now, Mester Ingram, we'd be very gled indeed if you could throw any light on the stoary 'at . . . your friend from the North Isles has told us. . . . " And he told it wird for wird identical. "Well," he says, "if two men with their sight an senses tell the identical stoary o this experience, we accept it, and the days o meracles is not past."

That's the stoary o James Smith. . . . That's still known by a good number of the old histoarians in the North Isles. . . .

Now . . . the stoary goes that this Marion Jamieson . . . was a bit of what was known in those days, quite coamonly through the Isles, you know, was a sort of a witchie woman. An she says, "Vengeance is mine, I will repay!" An she sat her down i the old quiet barn wi the hair loose down about her head, an she wouldn't eat—she fasted for several days . . . as she worked her vengeance on this Smiths. An she said 'at their big, fair, their fine mansion house of Smithfield now with aal its saervants, the waals o him would be turned into a dunghill and the birds of the air should have . . . the stons for a restin place, and ten coffins should be going within days to lay them aal to rest. And it wäs so. They

The Death of James Smith

departed this life, and their mansion house was without a roof . . . with the dunghill around him, an the birds in the air buildin in him, is there to be seen now. . . . They aal died out. . . . And the stoary goes, when they were goin to the funeral with wän, then . . . they were measurin the other wän for his coffin.

Some Orkney Weather

David Work, John Halcro

There was a New Year's Day, ice cam on the loch, you see, an aal the young fellows cam there skatin. They were aal oot there wan New Year's Day, ice on the loch, an they were skatin an there were wan of this boys 'at geed a bit too far oot, and in the middle o the loch the ice was soft, you ken, an it broake wi him an he geed doon, doon in a hoale, and the other edge o the ice just catched him onder his chin. He slid away under the ice till he came to another hoale, and his head did the same on top o the ice, an when they cam there his heid just stuck on again . . . the frost was that strong, you ken, till it just froze his heid on again!

In the evenin then they were sittin aroond the haerth tellin stories, and this boy was there too, and he was gotten some o the cowld wi his dip in the cowld watter, you know, and he start to sneeze. An he was gan to blow his nose—they just blow their nose wi their fingers then, you ken—an he was gan to blow his nose, an wi the haet, it was kind o thaaed the ice aboot his neck, you ken: he aimed his heid in the fire!

* * *

Sam'l Groat was oot Wast in a very heavy gale to the wast'ard: the wind caught them in the herrin boat, you know. He said: "Talk about sea! When we were on the top o the crest of the wave," he said, "we looked down on the Kame o Hoy, straight down on the mountain top. An," he says, "between seas, we had a crew of young aigile boys—they were on the sea bed as soon as the boat was dry, they just filled their baskets with cockles and mussels and jumped aboard when the next wave caught us. We looked doon the Kame o Hoy again, and then she took bottom again, and they just filled the boat with cockles and mussels between seas."

They said, "It must have been blowin."

"Blowin?" he says. "I . . . must believe it was blowin," he says. "It

78

blowed all the horns off the cows in Rackwick," he says: "they was all polled after that, it blowed the horns off the lot. . . . The cows stood head to wind, ye see, and the horns went, 'cause the ears foldit back and the horns stood out, and they went," he said, "they was all polled after that," he says, "the first polled cattle that ever was in Rackwick!" That was his gale!

The Trow of Windhouse

Brucie Henderson

Well, there a big house in Windhoose, but he's all doon now; an he hed a graet pasturage, an the proprietor 'at owned it . . . it wis a big, big estate, and he lived i'tö this house.

They were a hoose before, and this een was built in 1801. . . . There were aye annoyance intil the hoose, wi soonds and things goin up an doon the stairs, and they would say that the sarvants, when they . . . were passing up an doon the stair, they would . . . something like a man pass by them, and some o them was aaful frightened. But there were eens 'at was yondrawa, they caa'd them Spences to neem; that would ha' been in the aerly pairt of the lifetime. . . . They said 'at he cam hame fae Sooth, and he had, I think, six children. An he hed t'ree dowters an t'ree sons, and they were shörly come to manhood and womanhood.

An then there were something that took place every Christmas moarning at the house: they were a graet noise, and they were the same as if they'd been whirlwinds 'at cam over the hoose, that shook the bolts o the doors, and the hoose shook aalways atween twelve an wan o'clock. And when the moarning cam on Christmas moarning they were always a death i'tö the hoose, they were one found dead i the baed. So durin this time, for three Christmas moarnings, he first hed a dowter that was found dead i the baed on Christmas moarning, then he hed a son, then he hed a tablemaid that was sarved him for several years. An on Christmas Eve she did the serving, finished up all at night, an was in quhite good health. And this noise cam over the hoose. An when Christmas moarning cam they heard no sound, and they rose, and then . . . the hoosekeeper fand this tablemaid dead i'tö the baed.

Now this gentleman said, when anidder Christmas cam, 'at he was in no wise goin to bide in Windhoose on Christmas Eve to sleep over the night for Christmas. But he hed friends in Reafirt' in Mid Yell, an he was goin to take the family an his sairvants there for the night, an he hopit

80

that they would be no deaths this year. So . . . it was a very very wild night an it was a lot of snow, and they hed a . . . , probably a gig, but they hed to tak a horse wi a sledge to tak this people through the snow. And they were riggit this sledge and the horses to tak them all to Mid Yell.

And noo there a ship, it's been i the North Sea and it's been aaful bad weather aboot this time 'at Christmas is comin in, the Helly Days o Yöl. . . .

So there a knock 'at comes to the door when they're gotten all ready and they're goin to go, an Mester Spence said to een o the sarvants that she was bidden to go to the door. And she said, probably, "I'm sorry, hit's maybe the ghost!" An he said, "Oh no, Jean, don't be so silly, go to the door, you have a good nerve!"

So she göd to the door, an here's a man staundin, an she says, "Who are you?"

He says, "A'm a shipwrecked mariner, an," he says, " . . . I saa the lights. An," he says, "me," he says, "an my chum," he says, "wes aal that saved wir lives oot ot o the great ship 'at we were in. An," he says, "the staering gaer wis geen wrang, and," he says, "I've not hed food fae four o'clock the day before yesterday. An," he says, "shö struck," he says, "in the moarnin," he says, "aboot . . . but," he says, "it was moonlight," he says, "aathough it was a storm an gale, and it was clear," he says. "An," he says, "shö was water-logged from end to end, an," he says, "the masts was tore aal unless one, an," he says, "there were one bit o sail on the one. An," he says, "shö cam into this precipice an into this precipice—an shö was a graet ship an she hed this mast, an," he says, "me an my chum was splendid climbers—we could climb like this steeple eens that bigs this. . . . An," he says, "as shö cam wi the side o her on along," he says, "this graet precipice," he says, "we watched till she cam and we sprang, and we wan on a skelp. An," he says, "we stöd there an we lookit, it was a piece up 'at we hed to clim, an we thowt we might do. But," he says, "we saa a meeracalous sight," he says. "Shö struck three times, and then," he says, "shö just göd right in coomle an," he says, "we could see aal wir mates parishin below us.

"An," he says, "we climbed and we climbed up," he says, "an," he says, "we travelled," he says, "fram four o'clock this moarnin," he says, "first the wan wey an the öther, an there were no life to be seen." Weel, you

81

see, yon hoose is the hidmost hoose until you com to the territories o Nort' Yell along the banks. . . . "An now," he said, "we cöst lots, an we said, 'Weel, if wan o us dies wi fantation we'll boath die wi fantation, an we'll spleet.' An," he says, "wan went to the Nort'ard an I went to the South'ard. An," he says, "fae four o'clock o moarnin I'm sowt, an then," he says, "I saa a ray," he says, "the same as light, and I travelled on aathough I'm gotten that weak from starvin, an I'm cowld."

And she says, "Oh, come in, come in, come in." So he cam in. So Mester Spence quhestioned him, and he telled him this, an he said, "Oh that's all right, we'll get you clo'es," and they tell'd 'm aboot the punchbowl and they gae 'm a swig oot ot o this, and they said, "There plenty o stoff here now. You'll take tea, and then," he says, "you'll come wi wis."

And he says, "Come where? Now that we're claikin."

So he telled him aboot this accident, an this deaths bein oot o the hoose, an goin, an he said, "Oh man," he said, "you're talkin a lot o rubbish."

An he said no, he said he was talkin no rubbish, he said if he bade here he would die.

An he said, oh, he said, that was a lot o rubbish, he said, since if they would give him leave to bide i the house he would hairm noathing, an he would need his sleep.

And they said, "Oh well, if you wänt, we'll leave the keys with you, and here a nice big room here, and then there a wee fire in it always, and we'll put in a fire tae you,"—they were aaful nice til him—"afore we go. And then there meat here, and there every thing. An you can rise, whenever any invasion comes, I'll show you where you can protect yourself. There a place in here," he says,—"we don't have no guns or we have noathing practically," he says, "whatever. That's not needed, but," he says, "here's a place," he says, "in here," he says, "where there a graet eetch," he says, "that's as long as yourself: it cuts up the blocks o wuid for Christmas. An," he says, "if you're boathered at all, or if you hear anything, you can take him with you."

So this man fell asleep—they left i the last o the day light: yon would ha' been aboot four o'clock when he cam, an they made for Mid Yell an they left him. And he bade yondroo and he göd to baed aboot five when they were geen, an he sleepit fae then till aboot half-past eight, and when he rase at half-past eight he t'owt 'at he would take another feed. And he göd an he took some meat an things, an noo he was a graet smoker. He put up the fire and he settled doon and he hed in his mind aboot whatten fools this people is for tellin me this rubbish. So he sat there, an noo he t'inks, "I'll go to baed ageen." This is half-past eight, noo he's passin nine. He goes to baed ageen and he sleeps i the baed until half-past eleven.

An quen noo he rises and the moon is shinin as bright as day, and such a lovely clear frosty night, just like what Christmas Eve would ha' been. An he could see the hooses on the other side o the Voe, from the Herra, an he göd oot an walkit around yondroo and then he cam in an he t'inks in his mind, "I'll key up the doors an I'll go to baed noo an I'll sleep till moarnin. This is rubbish!" So he cam in, but he decided this noise cam aboot the hoose aboot twelve, so he says, "Oh, this is now a quarter to twel'. I'll have another look oot noo"—they were noathing.

And then he settled doon and then the light wis, and then he said the hoose began to darken, an darkened an darkened an darkened. And then, he said, he hed this lamp lowin, but they were no moon that was seen, an it was the sam as if the windows had been aa blindit—taerribly blindit. And then, he said, he heard a ro-ar, he said, intae the hoose, till the hoose shook lik thunder. And then he sprang in yondroo an he fetched oot this eetch, and he oapen't this door. An when he oapen't this door it was the same as there was noathing but like blackness aroond the whole o the house.

An he came oot thonderawa, an he began and he threw up this eetch in it, he threw up this eetch in it and then it liftit from the house and the house lightened up; an it was like a black lump. An he followed this black lump so faur, maybe a half o a mile, and then he said it fell down, and it fell down—well, this is the story, whether it's true or no—he fell down just like a hush of blubber. And he left it and he cam back, an he hed nether fear or noathing. An he took a feed an he göd to baed, and he sleepit till eight o'clock o a moarnin. An he rase an then he made himself tay and then yon eens cam.

An he said, "Now," he said, "you said 'at there were a thrall, or a thraw"—they hae a neem for it—"an," he said, "I didna believe you. Well," he says, "I'm killt the trow an we'll have to go an böry him." And they were supposed to gae an böry it, and ye can see where that was still, 'at's ahint fra the heid o the Voe o Mid Yell, an it's among haether, an that's just aboot the size of this floor, an it's as green as can be where this trow was supposed to fall.

But still this story is no finished. Yon's yon. The set 'at cam to big this hoose in eighteen-wan was a set from South, and they said that there were twenty that cam to build: they were shörly nearly two year buildin, and they said they were of a awful rough type o maen. But then it wid ha' been packets 'at they cam wi, and they came to Mid Yell. And they were a man 'at was very clever, an he countit them an he said they were twenty. An the moarnin that they güd he said they were nineteen. An they said, "Oh, a lot o rubbish! Yon man talks a lot o trash! Yon's no been aa that's been yonder."

But when they were feenished wi the hoose, they said, the night that they feenished the hoose, they hed an aaful cairry-on o drink an stoff afore it wis that they were to go the öther moarning. And they said that they were one o this men 'at was yondroo, 'at they were shörly been fightin or something wi the drink, and they were killed 'm. And they were toarn op the door, and they were liftit the ston 'at was anunder this graet door, and they were teen oot all the sand, and then they were geen doon as faur as whar the . . . stons was in him, and then they were teen them oot tö, and they were packit him in there.

Noo, this . . . it's not a terrible time ago, but it's a good quhile ago, it would ha' been when Mester Gordon wis tenant, this door began an it slippit down an it slippit down, and then the snow cam in anunder; an he wouldn't hev this, and then he fetched ones to fix this door. An of coorse they fixed it an they tore it up, and when they cam doon so far—he wanted them to put it that it couldna go—then they cam on the skeleton of a graet man. He took the skeleton oot an he's böried below the door. And so yon was supposed to be the een 'at hauntit the hoose. So that's the tale o't as far as I can tell.

The Oo-T'iggers

Tom Tulloch

Weel, this stoary wis telled aboot the Haa o Midbrake. This was i the days when the weemen-fokk güd aroond—weel, it raelly wis a form . . . o beggin, but i this parteeclar instance they were seekin oo, and it was ay referred til as . . . them goin on oo-t'iggin. And this two weemen this parteeclar day cam to the Haa o Midbrake, t'iggin oo, and they set them doon an sat fir a while and then the lady o the Haa o Midbrake, shö güd an feetched them some oo. But unfortunately fir hir, shö gied wan o them black oo and shö gied the ither een white oo. Noo aboot this säm time the Laird o Midbrake hed boats fishin til 'im at the haaf, and some o his boats fished fae Wuidweek across ipö the Wast side o Unst. He hed three sixtareens at Wuidwick at this parteeclar time. Noo efter the weemen got the oo, they sat fir a moamend and then the een 'at wis gotten the black oo, shö rase up in a very graet hurry an set aff through the door, the säm as if shö'd been kind o ill-plaesed.

The ither een sat fir a while, an then shö seemed as if shö wis meeditatin ipö somthing, and shö aalso jumpit up in a very graet hurry, an shö said the Loard wis bidden to be aboot them, shö said, they were evil brewin the day! And shö seemed to keen whar to go, so shö güd oot through the door o the Haa o Midbrake, and shö güd to the wast'ard up through the yaurd. An doon ower in, there a burn there, an when shö cam doon to the burn then the t'igger 'at wis gotten the black oo was sittin i the aedge o the burn, an shö hed three big yoag shälls floatin i the waater. And shö wis ay bällin in peerie stons tö mak waves, and shö wis disturbin the yoag shälls graetlie, and the wife 'at wis gotten the white oo got on til her an gied her a graet scowldin, an took her oot o the burn, an shö very carefullie liftit the yoag shälls oot o the waater an set them ipö dry launt.

Noo it was recordit 'at yon saem parteeclar day, 'at the Laird's three boats 'at wis fishin fae Wuidweek was oot at the haaf fishin an the

85

whoale three o them was just very nearly cast awey, but they did come to the shoer saefly. So it would appear as if the wife 'at got the white oo had no arrifed at the burn in time, that the wife 'at got the black oo would ha' bälled in enoff o stons til ha' upset the yoag shälls, an if shö'd managed that, then the laird's three boats'd lekly all t'ree been lost fae Wuidwick.

. . . Yes, the black wool wis of less value: it was very aften spun into the yaurn 'at they caa't the swaara, and the white swaara was of more vailue when they cam to sell it as what the black swaara wad ha' been.

The Milk and Butter Stones

Jamesie Laurenson

This was another witchcraft story, very typical of what went on in those days, an this was a very religious woman, a well-living woman, and she said to her dyin day that she hed this experience. She lived away at Colbastoft . . . her maiden name was Christian Ganson, and she married a Laurenson man . . . wän of the survivors of the *Diana*, the whaler that was frozen in. . . . It was the means of his death: he died a young man—but that was the woman. And she lived, as I say, at the East House of Colbastoft—that's the north side of Fetlar. And when she was goin to get married and be leaving that place—then she went to live at Houbie . . . —an old woman that lived in a small house at Grue . . . she toald her that she had to com and see her before she left. So she came. . . .

An she said, "Well, my jewel, you're leavin," and she says, "you've been a fine neighbour, a fine girl on the place. We'll miss you very much. And you're getting married, but I'm very sorry that I don't have very much to give you. But I have something 'at's very valuable: it's not money but it may be in a way it's even better as money. An while you keep it, it'll be of great help to you." And she says, "First of all, look at the door that there no boady coming in, becaz this is a secret."

She said, "No, there nobody." . . . So she went out and she oapened up a old sock, an then out of that she lowsed a piece o old flannelet an she took two stones. Wän was a yellow ston an the other was a white ston. "Now," she says, "this is what I'm goin to give thee: it's served me well, aa this years. But my day is gettin done now an it's no farther use to me, but it could be use to you, for you're a young woman, settin out on life's journey. Now," she says, "that yellow wän is a butter ston, the white wän is a milk ston. An this was stons specially enchanted by the Pic's (or the trows), and we . . . they cam our way—the peerie fokk gev wis them becaz we were pretty chummy wi them."

An she looked—she didn't know whether to take them or not—"No, no," she says, "you . . . you take them."

An she says, "Weel, what would I do with them?"

"Well," she says, "what you do if you're ever in need o a little o milk and your cow is not givin milk—take this white ston an heat him in the fire an dip 'm in waater an pat him three turns with the sun, three turns against the sun, and say—an whoever you want this milk taken from i the township, anyboady 'at has a good cow, just point wi the tongs to that house an say,

> "Tak aa fae until aa's teen
> Quhat might blaa dee fae the been."

That's what shö had to say. An when she wanted the spell broaken again she turned them opposite way, you see, an pointed to the house, that broak the spell. And the saëm with the botter—she wanted a good bit o botter from anyboady's cow or off their milk, you see, she did the saëm.

Well, she decided 'at she would take the stons. So she took them and tied them up in a bit o cloth very, very carefully, an . . . after that, of course, she got married to this man who lived at Houbie. (I could tell you the house they lived in, where . . . Martha Henderson lives. You see as aa this history's supposed to be true, now they know aa the houses where the people lived in.) And so she married, an if she didn't have time, an a young married woman, to bodder about these things—but in after years—a few years after, she thinks, "I winder whether owld Mäggie's steens—I winder if they were anything in that?" An she's pondering about that, an now she knew where she put them an tied them. She'll go wän fine afternoon an have a look at them. Yes, right enough, they were there, the yellow wän—the botter wän—and the white wän. And she's thinkin, "I winder if I could try it, just for curiosity?—Not that I waant the milk or the botter, but just to try it." She said, "Yes. The next time that I kirn"—she had a cow 'at wasna much wirth, you know . . . she was a very indifferent cow—"Yes, well, I'll have a shot at it."

So she mindit what old Mäggie said to her, what she had to do . . . You know they had . . . when they put the . . . milk in . . . the kirn, 'at they had to put a little o waarm waater in it, you see, to bring out the botter.

The Milk and Butter Stones

So she hotted the ston i the fire, i the tongs, put him in the waater, mindit what she hed to say—

> "Tak aa fae until aa's teen
> Quhat might blaa thee fae the been"—

pointed to this house in Houbie where there was a woman had a good milking cow. And she hadn't kirned very long till she knew that there was something going to happen that she had never seen . . . had this experience before. . . . You know before the botter comes on, you know, 'at there's a lot of froathy stoff 'at makes the botter. And this came up, up, till she thought 'at there was something odd here happening, so she was afraid if anyboady came in in the sitting-end, so she took. . . . (You know the kind o churns they had in those days with . . . a long basin made out of staves, like a barrelly thing but higher, . . . and the staff that they churned with at the time. . . .) So she got it taken ben, in the ben end, so that no boady would come in—if she heard any footsteps she was just goin to leave off churning an just go in the other end yonder, . . . like you could in here.

An she kirned awey—churned away an the botter startit to com on an she never saa such a lot o botter in her life. An she got excited. But . . . she calmed herself an she said, "Well, I'll have to go on with it now, but I couldn't continue doin this." An she kirned away an aal this botter came on. An she kept it out of the way, for noboady could know she was doin this, you know.

An a day or two after that woman 'at she'd . . . who they had taken the botter off the cow of, the neighbour, stood on a high part of the township an said, "Now hear what I have to say, you devils that you are! Some o you is taken by your Devil's arts my botter, tö my young children 'at needs it. But I'll—I'm going to the minister to lay you before the Session an he'll deal with you. An," she says, "I have a good idea who it is. But A'm not speaking about the young . . . fine young woman 'at's come in to the township, I'm exempting her, 'caz I know she wouldn't do a thing like that." An so . . . she gave them a proper telling off.

But naxt day when everything was quiet, Kirsty took a spade an went to the yard (an I could show you the yard i Houbie yet, mind, the cabbage place) an dug a holl deep, deep, deep, deep, an shö put the two stons in.

"Now," shö says, "no more witchcraft for me wi you boggerin things," an diggit them down under. And they're there in that yard yet. The two stons is in that yard in Houbie yet.

Q And where did you hear this from?

A ...Man, where did I hear this? God, ...Kirsty Ganson told it aa... —an she was wän o the most truthful weemen in Fetlar—yes, she told that story to me grändmother. Told it to her dying day...Yes, yes.

Witch Meets Witch

Tom Moncrieff

There were twa weemen in ee neeborhöd. And een was a kent witch. She lived be hersel in a peerie hoose, and nearby was a crofter's place—of coorse he was a fisherman, and awaa maist o the time. And she was a young woman and had a wee lassie—she wisna really a witch, but "she could dö mair as maet hersel", but she only used the power to keep her aen. And she had a coo claer to calve, and her wee lassie was ay rinnin in to the aald witch.

So ee day, the aald witch said to the lass, she says: "Whan your coo calves, du might tell me whan thy mither gyings to tak the first milk, but du manna tell any person." An of coorse, "the thing can tell a tale 'at canna bear a burdin"—the wee lassie couldna keep the story til hersel, so she tauld her mither. And her mither said: "O, faith, I sall tell thee whan to gying! That sall be aa right!"—'cause she'd in mind her preparations to counter the evil.

And when the coo calved and the calf was pitten by, oot o the rodd, she took her milk stöl, and she said: "Noo," she says, "lass, thu can gying and tell yon aald bitch that I'm gaan just to sit in anunder the coo this meenit!"

And the peerie lass ran alang the brigstane, and she cam in to the aald wife and she says: "Mammy is just settin her anunder the coo this meenit."

"O, thanks to thee, my jewel!" says the aald wife. She set by her wheel; she drew in a pail til her fit, and of coorse there was a raip—a rope stretched across the hoose for dryin clothes—she took a piece of thick rope and she heaved it across the raip, took the ends doon in front o her, and began to milk the sam as she'd been milkin on the paps of a coo, ower the pail. And the first that filled her haand was coo's dung. She says: "O lass, my Loard, thu's tellt thy mither!"

91

Peerie Merran's Spoon

Tom Tulloch

This was a story 'at was telt to the bairns to . . . encourage them to tak their gruel aboot the moarnin. They telt them 'at the faeries güd to cairry the Ness o Houlland—that's a long smaa ness 'at lies oot through the sea here at the north end o Yell—'at they were going to cairry him some wey, awey fae the aest'ard o Shetland to help to mak a brig ower Yell Soond. An when they cam yondroo this moarnin they set doon the Ness while they had their brakfast. But when they set them in to their brakfast, then they fand oot that they were een o them 'at wis lost her spün. So een o the leadin faeries said to the rest o them 'at they were bidden to

> "Caa fast an sup shün
> For peerie Merran wänts a spün."

But they were apparently i thatten a hurry 'at they boaltit doon their brakfast, an they never waetit quhile peerie Merran got a laen o wän o their ither spüns. And they liftit the Ness and set aff wi him ageen. But fir the wänt o her brakfast peerie Merran couldna tak her equal share o the wöight, and when shö got the full wöight upon her, shö wisna able to cairry it, an shö bruke her back. An fir the wänt o her cairryin ipö the Ness, the Ness fell, an peerie Merran fell anunder him. And peerie Merran is anunder the Ness yet, an the Ness is lyin yondroo broaken in three.

The Magic Island

Jamesie Henderson

I don't know exactly where, but it was supposed to be aff o some o the North Isles or the West o the Mainland, but there was a faimily, father an mother an two sons an a daughter. Well one mornin the daughter went away to take lempit for bait at the shore, an she didna come back when she should ha' come. So they gaed aff to look for her, but there was no trace o her ever fund: they thought, weel, the only thing was she had slippit ower the face o a rock and wis drooned.

Oh, some while efter that, maybe years efter that, the faither and the two sons gaed aff to the sea, fishin, wan day. Came a very thick fog, and they thought—they'd no compass in the boat, an there was very little wind, but they got oot the oars an tried to pull as near as they could for whar they thoyt the shore wis. Efter a whilie they did mak oot some land, as they cam in on a beach, but it was a strange place to them, they'd never seen it afore, but there wis a boat landin place there, so they brang the boat up an hed a bit o a look aroond. They saa a path, so they folla'd the path, an it led it up tae a good big hoose. They thoyt the best they could do wis knock at the door an see if they could get some informaetion as to whar they wis. So they knockit on the door, a man cam to the door an they tell'd him what had happened them.

"Oh," he said, "com in, com in," jist com in an wait tae the fog cleared an they would see whar they wis then. So they cam in: a grand weel-furnished hoose, an wha wis the mistress o it but the lass that was supposed tae have been drooned years ago. So when they saa that they thought there wis somethin kind o queer about it, an they didna like to ask ony questions.

But . . . she asked hoo they wis, an oh, they wis aal fine, an she said, oh, they would hev somethin tae aet, set doon a grand diet to them tae aet. An they wis taakin awey aboot different things, an the man said, did they hev ony baests that they would sell?

93

"Oh yes," the old fella says, "we hev a coo, a grand coo 'at A wis thinkin on sellin indeed."

"Weel," he says, "A'll buy her. What dae ye want for her?"

Oh, he named a good price for her, he would want that onywey—

"Oh," he says, "A'll give ye that," an he paid him in gold sovereigns.

So he thought, "Noo . . . A'll fin' oot whar this place is," so he says,

"Weel, ye'll hev to tell me noo what wey to com here, or A'll no be able to tak the coo tee ye."

"Och," he says, "don't you worry aboot that. A'll com for the coo masel."

So . . . wan o them said, "I think 'at the fog's offerin to lift a little."

So the . . . lass says tae them, "Weel, afore ye go, are they onything here in the . . . in the hoose 'at ye would fancy to tak wi ye?"

An the man said, "Oh, ye're welcome to onything 'at's here, jist pick onything ye would like an tak it wi ye!"

So the lass, she gied them a kind o look, I suppose thinkin 'at they would say, "Well A'll take—A'll tak you wi us!" Hooever they lookit aroond an they saa a grand big gold dish, an they said, oh, they would like tae hev that. So she handed it to them: "Well," she says, "tak it an go!"

So they gaed doon to the boat, and the man gied them a hand to laanch, an he said, "Jist pull ower that way a bit." So they pulled oot an the island disappeared in the fog, an the fog lifted an they were no distance aff o their own land. So they pulled for home, an soon as they cam in, the wife was meetin them at the shore very agitated. She says, "An aafu thing's happened. " She says, "Wir best coo's lyin in the byre deid!"

"Ach," the man says, "let her be gaan, she's ower weel paid for!"

So that was the end o that.

Mallie Coutts' Fairy Boy

Brucie Henderson

Mallie Coutts was a graet storyteller and she died maybe aboot forty-two year ago. And Mallie Coutts said 'at her grandfather was takin faels aff o a place afore he took oot his peats, and on the tap o this bank they were a crack, or what we call in Shetland a rivick. An when he cam 'at he was dellin this faels on the tap o this he haerd a groan, an he wonder't what this was—he thowt it was a sheep or something slippit into this. And then he haerd a voice sayin, "Watch me heid! Watch me heid! Watch me heid! Watch me heid!" An he lifted aff this fael an then the first 'at jumpit oot wis a boy, maybe aboot eight year old. An he wisna like wir boys, but he wis very queer an he wis cover't wi hair.

An he said til him, "I the name o the Loard, boy, whaur comes du fae?"

He says, "Never mind! Never Mind! Slip me! Slip me! Slip me!"

He says, "Na, A'll no slip thee, du'll be hungry."

"A'm no hungry," he says. "I ate the crip o hedder and the black bull's blaedder. Dat's whit I ate!"

An he says, "Well, whar comes du fae?"

He says, "I come," he says, "fae the Knowes o Troilasahoull—my . . . my place is fae the Knowes o Troilasahoull to the Grey Steen o Stourascord."

"Oh," he says, "boy, du's sayin a lock o rubbish." So he took him heem, and they warmed him mylk, an they gae him the mylk to drink atil a bowle, an he would drink da mylk oot ot o the bowle, and then he would spew it up, an he says, "Thu's gyaan to pooshin me, thu's gyaan to pooshin me, but A'll no bide lang wi dee! If it is 'at that thu hisna slipped me at wance," he says, "A'll blaa me breath," he says, "lik da Nort wind, an," he says, "A'll tak doon da hoose aboot dee." He says, "A'm no a boy, A'm a fairy chanceling, an my hom is atween—fae the Grey Steen o Stourascord to the Knowes o Troilasahoull 'at's in North Yell, an there's where A live an where A ging. An A wis onnly com ato this level to hae a sleep on me run."

And then he got to bed an he sleepit, an he snored to thatten a pitch 'at they thowt they would ha' to laeve the hoose. But another night cam ageen an then he said, "When are ye gaan to slip me? For if ye dönna slip me," he says, "A'll tak doon yir hoose an yir premises," he says, "an it's only eens like you or Mallie 'at could 'a' dealt wi me or teen hadd o me." He says, "I traivel aal Yell, an," he says, "I go frae the Grey Steen o Stourascord to the Knowes o Troilasahoull—an that's in North Yell, in Yinnick Staicks(?)" An he says, "If you slip me, good an well, an if ye dönna, A'll kill—A'll pat a curse on you an A'll kill every wan belongin you"—an they slippit him an they never saw him mair. An yon's the story dön an it was a queer bloody story!

*   *   *

I can nearly mind when [Mallie Coutts] died, but I never saw her. . . . She lived in Mid Yell, but she cam to veesit friends in Ulsta and then she tell't stories all through Ulsta. . . . A most terrible storyteller: she tell'd aa aboot fairies and things o that sort. . . .

The Last Trow in Yell

Tom Tulloch

This wis wan o the hidmast, if not *the* hidmast trowie hadd 'at wis in Yell: it wis in a knowe at Burnside in Collyifa [Cullivoe]. An aboot yon time they were a fiddler o graet repute in Collyifa be the neem o Rabbie Anderson, and the trows would aye meet him efery year an invite him to play tö them ipö owld Yül E'ën; an he wis graetly delighted wi this, fir although he would naither aet or drink in asaed them, everything 'at he laid his haund til through the coorse o the year prospered til him, and he thowt 'at this wis a very good bargeen, an he aye lookit forward to goin. But he never telled anybody whaur he wis been the Christmas Eve, an the fokk all kind o winder't whar Rabbie wis been, but he . . . never telt them at all. An they envýed him of coorse upon his graet prosperity durin the coorse o the year, but he held his tongue, he telt no body.

And then they were wän winter 'at he never saw anything tö the trows, and they never met him or ever invited him. And Rabbie wis gettin a bit alairmed aboot this, fir he was wonderin whit wey 'at it . . . would eyffect his prosperity fir the comin year. So they were ae night comin brawly weel on fir Yül 'at he made upon him an summed up his courage, and he güd in to the trowie hadd. An when he came in there, they werena a sowl in sight aless wän owld wife, an shö wis sittin on a doil-hoit at the fier, and he axed her whät on aerth wis come o all the rest o the fokk 'at was here the last time he wis? And shö said that he might ax; shö said they were a minister come to Collyifö, an he had thatten a volabeelity o preachin an prayin 'at the trows could not suffer it at all—they got no paece, and they were all hed to clear oot to Faera. The last wan o them wis gone, but shö t'owt 'at shö wis ower owld tö . . . start life in a new place ipö the face o the aerth, an shö t'owt 'at shö would just end her days whar shö wis. And that was the hidmast o the trows that ever was telled aboot in . . . North Yell!

That was supposed to be James Ingram: he was minister o the pairish o North Yell an Fetlar fae yghteen-t'ree to eighteen-twenty-wan. . .

Storytellers

COCKBURN, JACK (John W.) A Berwickshire gentleman farmer, and the only representative in this book of the south of Scotland. There are surely many others of the same kind, intelligent people with an interest in local antiquities whose knowledge comes partly from books but partly from word of mouth, but they are difficult to persuade to come forward, let alone make tape-recordings for a University department. Jack is only here as a friend and neighbour whom the editor happens to have known from the age of eight.

FINDLATER, Mrs. ETHEL (1899-1973). A notable Orcadian singer of Scots songs and ballads, whose memories happened to include one or two brief stories. Featured in *Tocher* 5, 1972.

HALCRO, JOHN GEORGE. One of a remarkable South Ronaldsay family, born 1915: knowledgeable on all sorts of local and seafaring lore. Featured in *Tocher* 26, 1977.

HENDERSON, BRUCE (1891-1977). A well-known storyteller in Shetland, who seldom moved far from his native valley of Arisdale in the south of Yell, but picked up much information from his father Jarm, the Mid Yell antiquary Laurence Williamson and others. Featured in *Tocher* 8, 1972.

HENDERSON, JAMES. Born in South Ronaldsay in 1903, retired to the nearby island of Burray after forty years in Edinburgh. His lore comes partly from his father, born in 1837, the son of a man evicted from Strathnaver in the Sutherland clearances, but partly also from his mother, a descendant of the gifted Halcro line. Featured in *Tocher* 26, 1977.

HIGGINS, BELLA (Mrs Isabella, 1887-1961). The oldest member of John Stewart's (q.v.) family to be recorded. The Stewarts were a rather unusual traveller family, sometimes farming in Perthshire, sometimes travelling in Ireland or Scotland, but most of their stories came from their own parents, John and his wife, born Agnes Campbell. See feature in *Tocher* 21, 1976.

LAURENSON, CHARLES. Youngest son of Mrs Kitty Laurenson, who managed to remember the fullest version recorded of "Essipattle and da Blue Yowe", the Shetland equivalent of "Cinderella", and many other tales: her son's traditions however come mostly directly from his grandfather, a native of Yell, and neighbours in Delting in the North Mainland of Shetland, where he still lives and farms.

LAURENSON, JAMES JOHN. Born in the Shetland island of Fetlar in 1899 and has lived there all his life, except for naval service in the First World War. Crofter, parish registrar and a notable local antiquary who has contributed in writing to Shetland papers and magazines and to the collections of the National Museum of Antiquities in Edinburgh, as well as recording his very lively and characteristic storytelling and some old ballads for the School of Scottish Studies. Featured in *Tocher* 19, 1975.

MONCRIEFF, TOM. A native of North Roe, the northernmost part of the Shetland mainland, who has lived since the War on his wife's family croft at the opposite end of the island, facing Sumburgh airport. Learned many traditions from old neighbours in his youth.

ROBERTSON, JEANNIE (Mrs Regina C. Higgins, 1908–1974). Best known as a very fine ballad-singer of traveller stock, she also told a number of fine stories heard from her mother and grandfather, with a character-istic warm-hearted feminine attitude to her characters. Featured as storyteller in *Tocher* 6, 1972: a book-length biography and appreciation is forthcoming.

ROBERTSON, STANLEY. Jeannie's nephew and the youngest storyteller in this book. He has remembered hundreds of stories heard around the camp-fire in his youth (see *Tocher* 31 (1979), 49-54) and learned more from travellers and others since: he has a particular interest in the supernatural, to which he is receptive himself. Lives and works in Aberdeen, and is frequently invited to folk clubs and ceilidhs where he gives a very professional performance both as storyteller and singer.

STEWART, GEORDIE. Another younger relative of Jeannie's of whom we have unfortunately lost track since the 1950s.

STEWART, JOHN. An older kinsman of Jeannie's and father of a notable family: apart from Bella Higgins (q.v.), his sons Alex, John and Andrew—of whom only John now survives—inherited his storytelling skill. Old John served in the Atholl Highlanders, travelled for many years in Ireland, and farmed for a time in Perthshire: he was also a notable piper, another skill passed on to his sons. (See feature in *Tocher* **21**, 1976). A few of John's tales were recorded by Maurice Fleming in 1955, the year he died, but many more have been passed on by his family.

TULLOCH, TOM. Lately sub-postmaster and handyman in Gutcher, Yell, inherited a deep interest in all aspects of North Yell tradition and dialect from his mother (née Andrina Fraser) and her sister: his storytelling style aims at authenticity rather than show. Featured in *Tocher* **30**, 1979.

VOY, GILBERT. Born at Inganess in the East Mainland of Orkney: despite the loss of an arm in an accident in Scapa Flow during the First World War has had a successful career as an engineer in Clydebank since. His traditions are mainly songs rather than stories, and his son Erlend of The Clutha has made some of them well-known.

WHYTE, Mrs BETSY (Bessie). A charming and articulate traveller woman, now living in Montrose, whose stories come mostly from her mother, of a Gaelic-speaking Argyll family of Johnstones. Her autobiography, *The Yellow on the Broom* (Edinburgh 1979), describes part of her childhood on the road; see also feature in *Tocher* **23**, 1976.

WILLIAMSON, DUNCAN. A traveller born near Furnace in Argyll who has wandered through much of Northern Scotland, gathering a vast repertoire of stories and ballads from many sources, and still lives by preference in a tent. Featured in *Tocher* 33, 1980.

WORK, DAVID. A successful Orkney farmer and cattle-breeder from the island of Shapinsay who remembered a variety of songs and anecdotes from his youth before the First World War.

The brief descriptions given here may often be supplemented from the "feature" articles in *Tocher* mentioned, which normally give biographical details of the storyteller, an assessment of his or her gifts by a fieldworker or friend, and several of his or her stories and/or songs and other memories.

Notes

ONE-EYE, TWO-EYES AND THREE-EYES

Told by Betsy Whyte, Montrose, as heard from her mother. Recorded by Linda Williamson, SA 1976/272 A1. Also intended for publication in disc form in the Scottish Tradition series.

This type is No. 511 in Stith Thompson's revision of Antti Aarne's *The Types of the Folktale* (second revision Helsinki 1964, usually referred to as Aarne-Thompson and abbreviated, as below, AT), the only comprehensive guide to *Märchen* or international folktales in general use. It is obviously related to its neighbour in the catalogue, "Cinderella", AT 510. As far as I know this is the first version of this form of the story to be recorded in Britain, though several English versions have recently been collected in the United States. The form of the story collected by the Brothers Grimm is fairly similar, and available in print, but the American parallels which, like this, include rhyming formulas of a kind typical of "fairy-tales" long established in English, suggest that this version comes from a native oral tradition independent of print. Unlike nearly all the other stories in the book it is a type specifically intended for children (indeed I first heard Betsy tell it to my four-year-old daughter, substituting her name for that of Two-Eyes) and so has been placed first.

THE ROBBERS AND THE OLD WOMAN

Told by the late Jeannie Robertson, Aberdeen, as heard from her mother, who probably had it in turn from her own father, a noted storyteller of the Stewart clan and the ultimate source of most of Jeannie's stories. Recorded by Hamish Henderson, SA 1959/15 B4, in the presence of the English folklorist Dr Katharine M. Briggs. Original transcription by Robert Garioch published in *Tocher* 6 (1972), 176–8.

This can be assigned to the international type AT 1653F, "Numskull

Talks to Himself and Frightens Robbers Away", though no version from nearer than Italy is catalogued and the details are clearly localised. Compare "Doctor Know-All", AT 1641, where chance remarks such as "that's the third", referring to something quite different, make three thieves think they are discovered and confess: Jeannie's relative John Stewart, teller of "The King and the Miller", had a version of this. The present story, one of the shorter among the handful recorded by Jeannie Robertson, typically displays both her talent for comic description and her unvarying warmth of feeling for the poor or afflicted.

THE GREEN MAN OF KNOWLEDGE

Told by Geordie Stewart, Aberdeen, who heard it from his grandfather. Recorded by Hamish Henderson, SA 1954/101 B, at a ceilidh in Jeannie Robertson's house. Original transcription by Hamish Henderson and Tom Scott published in *Scottish Studies* 2 (1958), 47–61.

This version of AT 313, "The Girl as Helper in the Hero's Flight", recorded very early in the history of work with the travelling people, is no longer the longest Scots folktale on record, but it may well still be the best told in the fast, racy, colloquial style. Geordie Stewart half pokes fun at the whole convention of the "Land of Enchantment" (unusually explicitly separated from the real world here) while still in the main handing on the story as he heard it. He characterises Jack the hero half as the conventional lucky simpleton, half as a realistic, cheeky, matter-of-fact Buchan farm servant, definitely of this world, who speaks much broader Scots than the English-spoken Green Man and his daughter. This is a well-constructed and detailed version of one of the most popular long international folktales (for some closely related Gaelic and Lowland versions see Hamish Henderson's discussion in *Scottish Studies* 2: no Scots version has been recorded since to my knowledge) apart from two apparent lapses of memory. One is the third task, where international parallels suggest that the ants may have been brought in to help Jack to separate grains or seeds of different kinds mixed together in a heap; the other is the motivation for Jack's search for the Green Man. In other versions the hero loses a card game and so puts himself in the

Notes

villain's power: he *has* to seek him out. Here the conventional simpleton in the ashes somehow practises cards with his dog—cleverly brought in at the beginning in anticipation of his memory-destroying lick near the end—and so is too good to lose: his pursuit of the Green Man, helped by the usual friendly "donors" of fairy-tale convention, seems to be prompted by pure bravado, which is hardly in character—or is it?

THE KING AND THE MILLER

Told by the late John Stewart, Blairgowrie, who heard it from his parents as a child. Recorded by Maurice Fleming, SA 1955/37/1. First published in *Tocher* 21 (1976), 169–71.

This version of AT 922, an ancient international tale best known in English through the ballad "King John and the Bishop" (Child 45) and exhaustively studied by the late Walter Anderson in his *Kaiser und Abt* (FF Communications No. 42, Helsinki 1923), shows most resemblance to what Anderson calls the "German servant redaction" (*deutsche Knechts-redaktion*): together with the close resemblances between other Scots tales and versions in Grimm and other German collections, this may suggest regular links across the North Sea. The many Gaelic versions of this tale, on the other hand, seem to be related to the "old French redaction": see the brief study of the Scottish versions in *Scottish Studies* 17 (1973), 147–54. I failed to realise in that study that the only two Scots versions noted were from John Stewart and his son Andrew, but in fact other travellers not closely related to them have since recorded similar versions: see also *Scottish Studies* 24 (1980), 47.

THE THREE DOGS

Told by the late Mrs Bella Higgins, Blairgowrie, who learned it from her father John Stewart, the teller of "The King and the Miller". Recorded by Maurice Fleming, SA 1955/31–2. First published in *Tocher* 21, 184–8 and 22, 234–6 (1976).

This story is clearly related to a Scottish Gaelic variant of the international tale-type AT 315, "The Faithless Sister", which includes the three helpful dogs with similiar names (though Able here replaces Leigheas, "Healing", in the Gaelic). There are however some very

105

The Green Man of Knowledge

individual features here, such as the fatal bone, and especially the final episode of the quest for the missing dogs, which has no parallel in the Gaelic. Mrs Higgins's younger brother, the late Andrew Stewart, remembered the story rather differently and perhaps less well, with a faithless *mother* and a rather misplaced king in the first part, but a more elaborate end where the dogs are given back their lost livers and lungs and then beheaded to turn them back into the long-lost brothers whom Andrew remembered to mention at the beginning: see the summary in K. M. Briggs, *A Dictionary of British Folk-Tales* . . . (London 1970).

THE PARSON'S SHEEP

Told by Gilbert Voy, a native of the East Mainland of Orkney, as heard from his father, who used to perform it at weddings "much to the disgust of my mother". Recorded by Alan Bruford, SA 1969/154 A2. First published in *Scottish Studies* 14 (1970), 88–93, with the tune of this and two further versions of the song (one from Orkney, one from Jeannie Robertson). I have since collected further Orcadian versions of this "cante-fable" or song with frame-story, AT 1735A, "The Bribed Boy Sings the Wrong Song"; it is also known in Orkney and North-East Scotland as a ballad, "The Parson's Wether", where the linking narrative too is sung (*Tocher* 4 (1971), 118–21). Mr Voy's version, which he recorded on an Orkney disc before the War, is learned by heart rather than improvised, so the dialect words are unusually thick on the ground and the hero's father untypically is given a precise fictional name.

THE CAT AND THE HARD CHEESE

Told by Betsy Whyte, Montrose, who learned it from her mother. Recorded by Peter Cooke and Linda Headlee, SA 1975/13/5—14/1, apart from the account of the giant-killing, Jack's return to his mother and a few phrases elsewhere, which are supplied from a more detailed but unfinished recording by Alan Bruford, SA 1975/200 B. First published in *Tocher* 23, 266–73 and 24, 320–3 (1976).

This story combines two international tale-types: the first part can be assigned to the vaguely-defined AT 577, "The King's Tasks", and the rest is a variant of AT 560, "The Magic Ring", where the ring (replaced by a box here) is generally recovered by a cat and a dog, helped perhaps by a mouse but not by the monstrous rat which has to be fought. The opening with the choice between a wee bannock with a blessing and a big one with a curse is common both among Gaelic storytellers and Scots travellers, including Jeannie Robertson, whose "Silly Jack and the Lord's Daughter" is another version of "The King's Tasks". Here the third task is evidently borrowed, not very convincingly, from "The King and the Miller". In the second recording used the giant's castle is not a ruin but the fine castle which Jack gets for himself when he is married, which perhaps adds to the unity of the story. The nonsense "run" at the end seems to be a Scots adaptation of a longer Gaelic ending formula which may include brogues of butter on a glass roadway (cf. *Scottish Studies* 9 (1965), 171.)

CHEESEPARER AND TEASTRAINER

First story told by the late Mrs Ethel Findlater, Dounby, Orkney. Recorded by Alan Bruford, SA 1969/53 B6. First published in *Tocher* 1 (1971), 31. Even this minuscule moral tale is an international type, AT 1452, with a distribution from Russia to the United States.

Second story told by James Henderson, native of South Ronaldsay, Orkney. Recorded by Alan Bruford, SA 1972/168 A. First published in *Tocher* 15 (1974), 246. This is a slight variant on the tale told in many districts that the first tea brought home there was boiled like cabbage and eaten with butter: the fact that it was common at one time to talk of "a dish of tea" can hardly have helped!

JACK AND THE DEVIL'S PURSE

Told by Duncan Williamson, Argyllshire traveller, who heard it from two or three older travellers. Recorded by Linda Williamson and David Clement, SA 1978/91 B4—92 A1; first paragraph supplied from an earlier recording by Linda Williamson, SA 1976/63. First published in *Tocher* 33 (1980), 150–5.

This story is an individual traveller variant of the well-known international type AT 330, "The Smith Outwits the Devil". In other Scottish versions such as that in J. F. Campbell's *Popular Tales of the West*

Highlands, No. XLII, told in Gaelic by another Argyll traveller, the blacksmith who hammers the knapsack or purse with the Devil in it is not himself the hero, but here the difference goes much further: the conversion of wicked imps to helpful elves is a reversal of the usual legend about the origin of fairies, that they were those angels who fell with Lucifer but were not wicked enough to go right down to Hell. The implication is that travellers are more likely than the settled population to see fairies mainly as helpful "fairy-tale" beings, while the Devil, though outwitted here, is definitely presented as a being to be feared and avoided. Duncan has a liking for stories which account for the origins of things, as well as those with an implicit moral. Jack here is a typical traveller hero, more Everyman than simpleton: in other longer tellings, like that from which the first paragraph is abridged, Duncan goes in detail into his original grinding poverty and his decline once he gets the purse into a drunken wastrel. He redeems himself by converting the imps and ends happily, unlike the hero in most versions of the story, too bad for Heaven and too good—or too much feared by the Devil—for Hell, who becomes the Will-o-the-Wisp, a homeless wanderer like the travellers. The emphasis on Jack kindling his own fire may be a vestige of an earlier version where Jack did become this wandering fire. The henwife who gives him the good advice is a recurrent figure in Scots and Gaelic tales, though outside some traveller tales she is nearly always a witch and a troublemaker, who for instance eggs on the wicked stepmother or makes her daughter cut off her toes so that her foot fits in Cinderella's slipper.

THE DEVIL AT THE FOUL FORD

Told by Jack Cockburn, Abbey St Bathans, Berwickshire, who heard the story from his grandmother Margaret Dodds of Fellcleuch, near Cranshaws, in the next parish to Longformacus. Recorded by Alan Bruford, SA 1966/19 B4.

The legend was well enough known in the mid-nineteenth century for the site to be marked with a monument erected by the father of the poetess Lady John Scott, who owned the farm of Wedderlie nearby. The names Foul Ford and Foul Burn already existed, implying no more than

muddy water, and a book apparently based on memories of Longformacus about 1810 (John Hutton Browne, *Glimpses into the Past in
Lammermuir*, 1892) merely mentions cautiously that the father, John
Neill, fancied he saw "a strange rider" on a "strange animal" one day in
the moor, and the family thereafter feared to go there—indeed, it is a
forbidding waste of bleak bog dominated by the dark cones of
Dirrington Great and Little Laws—until Henry the son was found dead
one morning there from no visible cause, having apparently taken off
some of his clothes in delirium. The full story in two varying versions
appears in *The History of the Berwickshire Naturalists' Club* **26** (1929)
301-3, 318-21. The only major additions in this later, or rather perhaps
more distant version are the marks on Henry Neill's face and the
introduction of the Duchess of Roxburghe in place of John Neill's sister
whose funeral he had attended.

THE ANGEL OF DEATH

Told by Stanley Robertson, Aberdeen, as heard from his grandfather,
Joseph Edward McDonald, who said that he knew the people concerned.
(The names given here may be invented, but the locality is the true one.)
Recorded by Peter Cooke, SA 1976/166/1. Also intended for publication
in disc form in the Scottish Tradition series.

The concept of Death as coachman is widespread in written as well as
oral literature, but no exact parallel to this story is in the international
index. It provides an excellent vehicle for the dramatic renderings which
Stanley Robertson gives in folk clubs and elsewhere, with the anti-
climactic ending serving perhaps to relieve the tension just as it reaches
bursting-point.

THE BRIDEGROOM AND THE SKULL

Told by Tom Tulloch, North Yell, Shetland as heard from his mother and
aunt and others in the neighbourhood. (This story was so well known in
North Yell that a local bard put it into verse.) Recorded by Alan Bruford,
SA 1978/68 B3. First published in *Tocher* 30 (1979), 371-2.

Highland and traveller versions of this so-called "Don Juan" tale (AT
470 or 470A), like most Irish and Continental ones, include episodes

where the hero on his visit to the next world sees and has explained to him the punishments of some of the wicked; Shetland versions are generally shorter, and in the extreme case the result of the hero's invitation to the skull is simply his death soon after—compare the two versions published by the late Dr Calum Maclean in *Scottish Studies* 1 (1957), 65–9 and *Shetland Folk Book* 3 (1958), 65–7. Here there is little to distinguish the story from other Shetland legends of visits to the fairy hill (e.g. *Tocher* 26 (1977), 104–5) but the hint of rewards and punishments in the Damoclean millstone and the fact that there seems to be less music in Heaven than in fairyland! The background in this world, from the delivery of the banns on the "Contract" night (usually followed by a party) to the sweeping of the hearth in the morning, is completely naturalised in its Shetland setting.

THE THREE YELLS

Told by Charles Laurenson, Delting, Shetland, who learned it from the late Robert Robertson of Quam, Collafirth, Delting. Recorded by Alan Bruford, SA 1974/196 B10. First published in *Tocher* 28 (1978), 217.

The idea of the "Friends in Life and Death" forms the basis of a number of international folktales, including a variant form of AT 470, the preceding story. Here the dead man's message seems less important to the story, a firmly localised legend like most of those which follow, than the dangers attending communication between dead and living. It is interesting that trows or fairies seem to be thought of as attending the gate to the other world—one of several hints that they represent a memory of the gods or ancestor-spirits of pagan times: Cudda or Cuddie is a name associated in the Northern Isles with trows, but sometimes also with the Devil.

THE DEATH OF JAMES SMITH

Told by James J. Laurenson, Fetlar, Shetland. Recorded by Alan Bruford, SA 1975/70 B1. First published in *Tocher* 29 (1978), 320–3.

No source was quoted, but everybody in the island of Fetlar still knows the outline of the story: either there is some truth in it—perhaps James Smith recovered briefly from a coma when he was thought dead—or the

Smiths were so unpopular that everyone wanted to believe it. Some versions mention that knocking was heard from inside the coffin at the funeral, but this detail has probably been transferred from another Fetlar tradition which suggests that a young woman may have been buried alive. The details of the curse, made with unbound hair and fasting against the enemy, are fully in accordance with the principles of ancient Gaelic and Norse magic. The historical details so carefully expounded by Mr Laurenson, who considers himself an historian rather than a storyteller, betray the weakness of oral tradition: the Revd. James Ingram succeeded the Revd. James Gordon as minister of Fetlar and North Yell after Gordon's drowning in 1803, and still later, in 1821, went to Unst; "Leatherhead", the Moderator of the Presbytery, cannot be identified at all; and apart from the fact that James Smith's son built Smithfield after his death, so that it cannot be the house cursed when James betrayed the boys to the Press Gang, as the tradition says, a possibly older tradition preserved by Tom Tulloch's family names the accursed house as the "Hoose o Toon", which was the manse of Fetlar (*Tocher* 29, 320; 32, 140)—so the curse really fell on the minister, perhaps Gordon, and his household, though in that version the traitor is a maidservant!

SOME ORKNEY WEATHER

First story told by David Work (senior), Shapinsay, Orkney, who heard it from an old neighbour from Sanday. Recorded by Alan Bruford, SA 1971/ 263 A7a. First published in *Tocher* 11 (1973), 86. Motif X1722* (b) in Ernest W. Baughman's *Type and Motif Index of the Folktales of England and North America*—one other version of this tall tale is cited there, from Indiana.

Second story told by John George Halcro, South Ronaldsay, Orkney, who heard it from Samuel Groat himself. (Tall tales today are usually told at second hand, as heard from a celebrated local liar.) Recorded by Alan Bruford, SA 1967/116 B2h. First published in *Tocher* 12 (1973), 127. The Kame of Hoy is a 900-foot high cliff: Rackwick is a village near it. Neither part of the story can be identified in Baughman's index, though the wind that blows off buffaloes' horns on the prairies seems to have featured regularly in Shetland sailors' yarns about America.

THE TROW OF WINDHOUSE

Told by the late Brucie Henderson, Arisdale, (South) Yell, Shetland, who heard the story from Laurence Williamson, the Yell antiquary, and others. Recorded by Alan Bruford and Tom Anderson, SA 1970/240 B4—241 A1; first, third and fourth paragraphs from SA 1955/95/2, recorded by Calum Maclean fifteen years before, which generally gives less detail elsewhere but more at the beginning. First published in *Tocher* 8 (1972), 252–6.

For the story as noted by Laurence Williamson himself see L. G. Johnson, *Laurence Williamson of Mid Yell* (Lerwick 1971), 137: Brucie, noted for his ability "to make a story out of anything", fleshed out the bare bones with dramatic details, invented dates and spurious connections at which more sober local historians like Tom Tulloch may jib, but which help to make it more impressive. Why the seemingly monstrous apparition is called a trow, which usually means a small fairy or goblin, is not clear: certainly it came at Christmas, when trows were said to be particularly mischievous. There are many tales about Windhouse, and the supposed quarrel among the builders—actually when the house was rebuilt, long after 1801—cannot really explain the haunting in Laurence Williamson's story, which happened in the eighteenth century.

THE OO-T'IGGERS

Told by Tom Tulloch, North Yell, Shetland, Recorded by Alan Bruford, SA 1974/206 A2. First published in *Tocher* 30 (1979), 346.

Tom Tulloch was actually born and brought up in the Haa of Midbrake, a former laird's house which his mother's family had been given until the landlords repaired their croft house—which was never done. There are many stories in the Northern and Western Isles of boats wrecked by witchcraft, especially the sixtareens or sixerns which went up to forty miles out to sea from Shetland in the eighteenth and nineteenth centuries for the long-line "haaf" fishing with only oars and a square sail. As here, most of the methods described involve sympathetic magic, though the boats are more often represented by caups (small wooden bowls), or in the Hebrides eggshells, splashing about in a tub of water than by mussel shells in a stream.

THE MILK AND BUTTER STONES

Told by James J. Laurenson, Fetlar, Shetland, who evidently heard it from his grandmother. Recorded by Alan Bruford, SA 1970/246 A2-B1. First published in *Tocher* 19 (1975), 86–8.

This, like the next story, depends on the widespread belief that the "profit" or "fruit" of various substances, mostly foodstuffs, could be taken away by witches (and by fairies, here identified by the storyteller with the Picts). Most of the stories have to do with cows' milk: taking the profit of it might mean, as in the next story, the ability to tap your neighbour's cow for milk, but more often it meant that the strength of her milk passed into yours, so that you got a lot of butter and she got none. As in Shetland it was normal to churn the whole milk and not just the cream, the butter often failed to "come" for various natural reasons, and accusations of witchcraft were therefore rife in many districts almost up to the last War. "Blaa-dee fae the been" may mean "bleed (Norse *blöde*) from the bone"—the taking of milk might stop short of this, just!

WITCH MEETS WITCH

Told by Tom Moncrieff, native of North Roe, Shetland, as heard from a neighbour woman born in 1830 when he was a boy. Recorded by Alan Bruford, SA 1970/231 B4. First published in *Tocher* 3(1971), 97. To say that someone could "do mair as meat hersel" implied that she had some supernatural power without actually using the word "witch". Other witches are said to have been able to draw milk from neighbours' cows by milking the pot-chain over the fire, or just opening a tap in a stake of wood driven into the earth floor of the house.

PEERIE MERRAN'S SPOON

Told by Tom Tulloch, North Yell, as heard in his own family. Recorded by Alan Bruford, SA 1973/59 A7. First published in *Tocher* 28 (1978), 205.

"Merran" is the local form of "Marion". This story ingeniously combines two purposes: it accounts for the shape of the Ness of Houlland (visible from Tom's birthplace and continued by a line of islands so that it does seem to be broken) by a variant of the origin legend of the broken fairy bridge, which elsewhere usually explains a sand-bar; and it proves the value of the breakfast porridge, though poor Merran did not do without hers because she wanted to! The fairies in this story seem to be as strong as giants.

THE MAGIC ISLAND

Told by James Henderson, native of South Ronaldsay, as heard from his father. Recorded by Alan Bruford, SA 1971/262 A1. First published in *Tocher* 26 (1977), 95–6.

Similar tales of a rarely-seen island are told in the North Isles of Orkney of "Heather-Blether" and in the Hebrides of "Rocabarraigh" (now identified as Rockall) and other names. The closest parallel to the form of this story, however, is in a tale from just across the Pentland Firth, "'E Silkie Man", collected in Canisbay parish by the Revd. David Houston and published in Volumes II to III of the Viking Society's *Old-Lore Miscellany* (London, 1909–11). There however the woman's husband is explicitly a seal at times and lives in an identifiable chasm on the coast of the isle of Stroma. This story and those which tell of women taken into the "fairy hill" when their families thought them dead reflect two sides of the pagan Celtic otherworld, the overseas "earthly paradise" and the underground realm of the dead. Evidently dead animals can go there too!

MALLIE COUTTS' FAIRY BOY

Told by Brucie Henderson, South Yell, Shetland, as heard from his father who knew Mallie Coutts herself (who had "thousands" of stories). Recorded by Calum Maclean, SA 1955/103/1, except last paragraph before asterisks, which is taken from a later recording, lacking the beginning of the story, made by Alan Bruford, SA 1974/204 B4. First published in *Tocher* 28 (1978), 224–5.

Such apparently realistic accounts of the finding of fairies, or children of some underground race, have been recorded in Britain at various times since the Middle Ages. This boy is unusually formidable and independent. He can hardly be a changeling, as he seems to say, and indeed there is no mention of any other fairies in his underground "run", which lies below a good part of Yell, from Stourascord above Brucie's home at Arisdale in the south to Troilasahoull, which may be Trollakeldas Houlla above Basta in the southern part of North Yell or an unidentified place further north—evidently associated with trolls or fairies.

THE LAST TROW IN YELL

Told by Tom Tulloch, North Yell, Shetland. Recorded by Alan Bruford, SA 1978/63 B6. First published in *Tocher* 30 (1979), 370.

Stories all over Britain and Ireland tell that the fairies have left (which does not mean that they are not still seen): from Ulster to Britain, from England to France, from Caithness to Orkney, from Shetland to the Faeroes. Various reasons are given, not all to do with religion as here. James Ingram, mentioned in "The Death of James Smith", was a noted evangelist who joined the Free Church at the Disruption and continued preaching in Unst along with his son until his death at the age of 103: he is mentioned in a similar story from Stackaberg in Fetlar. Here the story is combined with the common Shetland legend of the fiddler invited to play for the fairies. In North Yell both fairies and trows were spoken of, but the latter were thought of as being more "earthy" and dangerous— hence their home was described by the word for a wild animal's lair—and perhaps they were banished but the fairies remained: certainly more stories there seem to name fairies!

Glossary

In the glossary, = is used when a Scots word is a recognisable form or pronunciation of the English equivalent; — is used when it needs translation or explanation; : is used when a word looking like one in standard English has a different meaning or usage in Scots. Bracketed words in italics rhyme or otherwise indicate the pronunciation of part or all of the Scots word. The following letters are used to show that a form is peculiar (at least in this book) to a particular dialect:
(A) Aberdeenshire and the North-East; (O) Orkney; (T) traveller cant; (Y) the island of Yell only; (Z) Shetland.

A

A = I
aa, a' = all
aafa(e) = awful(ly)
aal = all
aal(d) = old
aathing — everything
abeen — above
ablow — below
aboot = about
abün (Z), abune — above
adae (whit's adae?) = ado (what's the matter?)
ae — one; of
aen = own
aerly = early
aerth = earth
aes — ashes

aest, aest'ard = east, eastward
aet = eat
aff, aff o = off
afore — before
aften = often
ageen (Z) = again
ahin(t) — behind
ain = own
airn = iron
airt; airts — direction; region
alane = alone
alang = along
aless (Z) — except, unless
an : and
anidder (Z) = another
anunder (Z) — under
asaed (Z) — beside
'at — that

116

atil, atö (Z)—in, into
atteensheen (Z)—attention
aul(d) = old
aw = all
awa(a) = away
awhantit (Z) = acquainted
ax = ask
ay (:*eh*), **aye** (:*l*) (1)—always
aye (2)—yes

B

baa, baal = ball
bade—lived, stayed
baed = bed
baerd = beard
baest = beast, farm animal
baet = beat
bairn—child
baith = both
bäll (OZ)—throw
banks (OZ): (steep)seashore
bannock—unleavened loaf, oatcake
bargeen (Z) = bargain
bay: baa, bleat
be: by; compared with
beast: farm animal, cow
becaz(e) = because
been(Z) = bone
belang (wha belangs this?) = belong (who does this belong to?)
ben—inside, through the house
bi = by
bide: stay; live
big(verb)—to build

bite: something to eat
bittie—little bit, a little
bizom = besom, brush
blaa = blow (but see note to "The Milk and Butter Stones")
blashie—wet, rainy
blin' = blind
bocht = bought
bodder (Z) = bother
bonnick = bannock, *q.v.*
bonnie, bonny—handsome, lovely, beautiful
böry(Z) = bury
böth(Z)—merchant's house, booth (used of a solid well-built house)
botter = butter
bowle (:*howl*)—bowl
bözom (Z) = besom, brush
braa; braaly—fine, beautiful, considerable; really (Z)
brae—hill, slope
brakfast = breakfast
brander—gridiron, griddle
brang—brought
braw = braa, *q.v.*
breeks, breekies—trousers
breid (:*feed*) = bread
bricht = bright
brig = bridge
brigstane(s)—path of cobbles or flat stones through muddy farmyard
brither = brother
broak, bruke (Z) = broke
buddy = body, person
buits = boots

117

C

caa = call; keep something moving
cairry = carry
callop = collop, *q.v.*
cam = came
cannae — cannot
castel (:*master*) = castle
caul(d) = cold
'cause, 'caz(e) — because
chap : knock
claa — scratch
claer = clear; ready
claes = clothes
claik — gossip
clap : pat (an animal)
closs = close
collop — a piece of meat
come : came
coomle (Z) — capsize, overturn
coont = count
coorie — crouch, huddle
coorse = coarse; rough (of weather)
coort = court
cöst = cast (past tense)
cot : cottage
coup — overturn
cowld = cold
crack : chat
cratur = creature
creak o day — break of day
cried : called, named
crip? = crib
croft — small farm, smallholding
croon = crown

D

daid (Z) = dead
dam : millpond
dee (1) = die
dee (2), deen (A) = do, done
dee (3) (Z) = thee
deem (A) — girl (dame)
deid (*deed*) = dead
deid saelins o the nicht — dead of night
deit = died
dellin (Z) — digging (delving)
dinnae — don't
dis (:*fizz*) = does
dis (Z)(:*hiss*) = this
dizen = dozen
dochter = daughter
doil-hoit (Z) — a depressed mood
doitin = doting, feeble-minded, crazy
dön (OZ) = done
done : worn out
dönna (OZ) — don't
doon = down
doot (A doot ye'll no) = doubt (I'm afraid you won't)
dottle(d) — feeble-minded, wandering
dour — stern, morose
dowter (OZ) = daughter
drap = drop
drookit — soaked
droon = drown
dry-hunt (T) — sell door-to-door
du (Z) = thou
dyke — field-wall

E

'e (A) = the
ebb : low tide
echty = eighty
ee, een (1) = one
ee; een (2) = eye; eyes
eence = once
E'en — Eve
ees (A) = use
eetch — adze
efery = every
'en (A) = then
enoff (Z) = enough
every : either
eyffect (Z) = affect

F

fa (A) = who
faa = fall
fae — from, since
fael; faelie — turf (noun & adj.)
faered; faer'der — afraid; more
    afraid
faimly = family
fan (A) = when
fand = found
fantation (Z) — starvation,
    exhaustion through lack of food
far (A) = where
faur (Y) = far
feared — afraid
feel (A) = fool; foolish
ferlie — marvel, curiosity
fier = fire
fin (A); finever = when; as soon
    as

fin' = find
fir = for
fit (three-fittit pot) = foot (three-
    legged pot)
fit (A) = what
fleet — agile
fleg — a fright; frighten
flöir (Z) = floor
fokk (Z) = folk, people
folla(e) = follow
forrit = forward
fort' (Z) — outside
fra(e) — from
fricht = fright, fear; frighten
fun(d) = found

G

gaan = going
gae (1), gaed = go, went
gae (2) = gave
gaen = going
gairdner = gardener
gan — go; going
gane = gone
gang — go
gaun, gaunna(e) = going; going
    to
geed (:*gear*) — went
geen = gone
geeny = guinea
gev (Z) = gave
gey (*guy*) — very; great
gie (*ghee*), giein, gien = give,
    giving, given
gin — by (the time); if
ging — go

119

gled = glad
glen — valley
gless = glass
gloamin — twilight
göd (OZ) — went
goon = gown, dress
gotten — got (past part.)
graet (Z) = great
greet : weep, cry
gress = grass
Güd (Z) = God
güd (Z) — went
guid = good
gyaan (Z) = going
gying (Z) — go

H

ha' = have
haa = hall; two-storey house (Y)
haaf (haaf fishing) — ocean
  (deep-sea cod and ling fishing
  with long lines in open boats)
had(d) — hold
hadd (Z) — lair, den
hae = have
haen — had (past part.)
haert = heart
hame = home
hannae — haven't
hap — cover, wrap up (with
  clothes, etc.)
haud (on) — hold; keep going
haund (Y) = hand
hed = had
hedder (Z) = heather
heem (Z) = home

heid (ower the heid o) = head
  (on account of)
helly (Z) — festival, holiday
hersel = herself; by herself
he's = his
hev = have
hid (1) : had
hid (2) : it
hidmast (Z) — last (hindmost)
Hielan = Highland
hilt nor hair — any trace (*cf.* hide
  nor hair)
hing = hang
hinna — haven't
his : has
hisnae — hasn't
hissel — himself; by himself
hit : it
hiv = have
hiz — us
Hogmanay — New Year's Eve
hoid (Z) = hide
holl (OZ) = hole
hom (OZ) = home
hoo = how
hoose; hoosie = house; little
  house
hort (Z) = hurt
houb (Z) — narrow tidal bayhead
humphed; humphy — hunched;
  hunchbacked
hunder = hundred
h'unt = haunt
hurl : a ride (in a vehicle); take for
  a ride
hush : a mass

120

Glossary

I

i (OZ); in i (Y)—in
in-aboot—into the house
intae, intil = into *or* in
ipae, ipö (Z)—on
'is (A) = this
ither = other
i 'tö (Z)—in(to)
itsel = itself
izel—cinders

J

jaiket—jacket
jist, juist = just

K

kebbick—a cheese
keek—peep
keen(Y) = ken, know
keeng = king
ken—know
kennel, kennle: kindle
kent—knew; known
key (verb)—lock
kin (1); kinna: kind; kind of
kin (2): can
kirk; kirkyaurd (Y) = church;
   churchyard
kirn = churn
knowe = knoll, hillock
kraw (Y) = gnaw
kye—cows, cattle

L

laen = loan
laeve = leave

lang = long
lassie—girl
lauch = laugh
launt (Y) = land
learn: teach
lee, leear = lie, liar
lekly (Z) = likely; probably
lempit (OZ) = limpet(s)
lether = ladder
licht = light
lik (OZ) = like
lilt: skip, trip
loch—lake
(a) lock (OZ): a lot
loss: lose
lowin (:*ploughing*)—burning
lowse (:*rouse*)—undo,   release,
cast off
luk = look
lum—chimney, smokehole

M

ma = my
maen (Z) = men
maet—food; feed
mair = more
maist = most
mak, makkin = make,   making
manna—mustn't
mare (Z): pony (in general)
marra = marrow
me: my
meat: food (of any sort)
mebbe = maybe
meenit = minute
meer = mare

meeracalous (Z) = miraculous
mither = mother
moamend (Z) = moment
mony = many
moose = mouse
(the) morn, (the) morra —
    tomorrow
moss : bog
murn = mourn
muskin, mutchkin — half-bottle
    (approx. — strictly rather more,
    quarter of a Scots pint or three-
    quarters of an imperial pint)
mycht = might
mylk (:*mile*) (Z) = milk

N

nae — no (adj.); not
nane = none
neebor; neeborhöd (Z) =
    neighbour; neighbourhood
neem = name
neen = none
nether : neither
news (verb) — to chat, gossip
nicht = night
niver = never
no : not
noo = now
note : cry, oath

O

o = of
oan = on
'on (A) — that (thon)

oncet — once
ony, onybody, onywey =
any, anybody, anyway
oo = wool
'oor = hour
oot = out
oot ot o (Y) — out of
owen (Y) — own
ower, owre (:*power*) = over;
    too
ower weel (OZ) — very well,
    pretty well
owld (OZ) = old

P

packet : regular boat service
paece = peace
paën = pain
park : pasture field
parteeclar = particular
pat = put (past tense, usually)
peer (A) : poor
peerie (OZ) — little
pinkie — little finger
pit; pitten = put (present; past
    part.)
platefae = plateful
pooshin = poison
proclamaesheen, procleem
    (Z) = proclamation (of banns),
    proclaim
pu' = pull
puddick — frog
push your fortune — seek your
    fortune (old texts have
    "spouss", i. e. espouse)

Q

quate = quiet
quen (Z) = when
quhat(Z) = what
quhile (Z) = while
quyne (A) — girl

R

rade = rode
raip (Z) — clothes-rope, drying-rope (indoors)
rase (up) (Z) — got up, stood up
recepsheen (Z) = reception
redd — clear; rid
refreshment : drink, dram
richt = right, real(ly)
rin = run
rive — tear
rivick (Z) — cleft, fissure
rodd (Z) = road
roon(d) = round
roostie = rusty
rost = roast
run : ran
rycht = right, real

S

saa = saw
sae = so
saëm (Z) = same
sairtan (Z) = certain
sall = shall
säm (OZ) = same
scowld = scold
schuil (*skill*; (A) *squeal*) = school
screp — scratch
scrythe (OZ) — swarm

seec — such
see'd — saw
seek : sick; disgusted
sel = self
set (him/her) (Z) — sit (down)
Setterday = Saturday
shäll (Z) = shell
sharger (:*bargain*) — weakling, runt of the litter
shö (OZ) = she
shörly (Z) = surely
shouthers = shoulders
shuffel = shovel
shuin, shün — soon
sic, sich = such
sixtareen(Z) — six-oared open *haaf* (*q.v.*) fishing boat
skelp (noun) — (1) blow, wallop; (2 — for "skelf"?) ledge
slip : let go
smaa = small; narrow
smiddy = smithy
snoot — nose; peak of a cap
somthin = something
sooth = south, the South (in Shetland — mainland Britain)
sowl = soul, person
sowt (Z) = sought
spaek = speak
speir — ask; ask after, greet
spleet = split (up)
sprinter = splinter
spün (Z) = spoon
staering gaer (Z) = steering gear
stan' = stand
stane = stone

123

staund (Y) = stand
steen = stone
stey = stay; live (in . . .)
stöd (OZ) = stood
stöl (OZ) = stool
ston (OZ) = stone
stoor — dust
strae = straw
streenger (Z) = stranger
suin = soon
sut = sat
swaara (Z) — coarse knitting
wool (used especially for
underwear)
swey — swivel (for hanging pots
and kettles over the fire)
syne; fae syne — then; since (then)

T

't = it
taak = talk
tae = to: for; until; too
taen — taken; taking
tak = take
tangs = tongs
tap = top
tatties — potatoes
tauld = told
tay = tea
tee (AO) = too
teen — taken
telled, telt = told
tellin — a warning, telling off
thaa = thaw
thack, thackit — thatch, thatched
thae — those

thatten (Z) — so much
the day, the morn, the nicht —
today, tomorrow, tonight
the were — there was, there
were
thee : thy
there : there is, there are
they were : there was, there
were
thocht = thought
thon (:*then*) = that
thonder; thonderawa (Z) —
yonder; that way
thowt (OZ); thoyt (O) = thought
thu = thou
t'ig; t'igger (Z) — solicit, collect;
collector
til — to
tö (OZ) = too; to, for
toddle : saunter
t'oomb (Z) = thumb
toon; toonship = town; township,
hamlet, group of crofts (q.v.)
tost = toast
towböth (Z) = tollbooth, prison,
customs-house
t'owt (Z) = thought
traivel; traivler = travel; traveller
trement = torment
trittle — walk with short steps,
trot
troch = trough
trow; trowie (OZ) — fairy, goblin
(troll) (noun and adj.)
tuik = took
twa = two

Glossary

U

uncan (OZ)—strange, new (to a place)

V

veesit = visit
voe (Z)—narrow inlet, sea-loch
volabeelity (Z) = volubility
voyal = vial

W

'wa = away
wa', waa, waal = wall
waak = walk
wal = well
wale—choose
walt = welt, hit hard
wan, wän = one
wance = once
wark = work
warna they? (Z)—wasn't there?
wast = west
wauken = waken, wake up
wee—little
weel = well
weemen = women
(I) weisht I—I wish I had...
wes = was
wey (:*why*) = way
wha = who
whan = when
whar = where
whatten (Z)—what sort of
whaur = where
wheasel = weasel
wheesht!—be quiet!

whenever: as soon as
whit; whit wey = what: how, why
wi = with
wid = would
win: one
windae = window
winder (Z) = wonder
winnae—won't
wir—our
wirth (Z) = worth
wis (:*fizz*): **wisnae** = was; wasn't
wis (:*hiss*)—us
wöight (Z) = weight
wrang = wrong
wuid = wood
wumman = woman

Y

yalla, yallow = yellow
yard: garden
yaurn (Y) = yarn, wool
yez(e)—you
yghteen (Z) = eighteen
yin (1)—one
yin (2)—that, those
yir = your
yoag (Z)—horse-mussel, large mussel
Yöl (OZ) = Yule, Christmas
yon—that, those
yondrawa, yondroo (Y)—(away over) there
youse = you (plural or singular)
yowe = ewe
Yül (Z) = Yule, Christmas